D0989576

Books by Ernestine Gilbreth Carey

Cheaper by the Dozen (with Frank B. Gilbreth, Jr.)

Belles on Their Toes (with Frank B. Gilbreth, Jr.)

Jumping Jupiter

Rings Around Us

Rings Around Us

Rings Around Us

by

ERNESTINE GILBRETH CAREY

BOSTON · Little, Brown and Company · TORONTO

LIBRARY OF CONGRESS CATALOG CARD NO. 56-5626

Published February 1956
Reprinted February 1956

Published simultaneously in Canada
by Little, Brown & Company (Canada) Limited

PRINTED IN THE UNITED STATES OF AMERICA

To our Manhasset neighbors and friends

Foreword

Last August, when the Carey family was sight-seeing in California, we came upon the huge cross section of a tree. "Look at this humdinger, Dad," Charlie, Jr., said. "It's older than you even, isn't it?"

"Slightly, son. By about six thousand years."

"Can rings like these be growing in me and everybody, do you suppose?"

"I like to think so."

Contents

Rings Around Us

CHAPTER 1

Soon We'll Marry

"When Mr. Right comes along," an elderly aunt used to say, "you'll know it in every bone of your body. Good men are scarce, child, so don't be caught napping."

"If you were napping the night we met," my husband has said since, "there wasn't the slightest sign of it, Ernie. When I paused to say hello, you reached out and grabbed me."

Nothing could be further from the truth. Instead it happened like this:

In September 1929 several Smith College friends and I went to a supper party in Greenwich Village. It was here that I found Chick looking over the current crop of girl graduates. Someone introduced us with the comment: "You're too much alike, so maybe I shouldn't do this. Anyhow, Ernestine Gilbreth, this is Charles Carey."

"What ho," Chick said, gripping my hand, "that's some red dress you're wearing, honey. Whee!"

"Do you like it?"

"What I can see, I like. Can you sit down in it?"

"I haven't tried yet. I bought this a week ago in Paris."

"That shade should look awful on a redhead. But it doesn't. Are you living in New York now?"

"Yes. Three girls and I have taken an apartment around the corner. We're having a fling at our first jobs too and pay checks look beautiful."

"I work uptown. Why don't you ring me sometime?"

"I'm not the aggressive type."

"In that dress? I don't believe it."

"You will . . . when you know me better."

"I intend to know you better. Where have you been all my life?"

After the confines of home and four years of college, this taste of Bohemian chatter hit like a champagne cocktail. Now I'm really living, I thought. I'm glad I wore this Frenchy getup tonight, even though it's sort of blinding.

"Ernestine," Chick said, pondering my name. "Are you any relation to the singer?"

"Afraid not. My mother's an industrial engineer."

"Did she ever tell you that good men are scarce?" he asked before our hostess led us off toward the dining room.

As we finished our ice cream and coffee, we heard that we would have to play bridge. With tallies in hand, Mr. Carey went off to table 1, I to table 8.

Since my bones seemed to be transmitting some urgent

news during the next few hours, I couldn't concentrate on my cards. Can't I get this gangling blond out of my mind? I wondered, as Chick continued to sit at the top table, while I stuck in Siberia. Must I make three grand slams doubled, for goodness' sakes, in order to see him again?

Eventually he captured first prize and I got the booby. As we compared our spoils, we swapped addresses and made our first date. With my knees still clanking like castanettes.

Perhaps similar types of people attract each other. In any case, Chick has the tall build, freckles and reddish hair characteristic of the Gilbreths. And a way of smiling and making friends immediately.

Soon we had begun to dream about a honeymoon in New Hampshire where he had vacationed as a boy. Occasionally we'd remember that groceries and New York apartments cost money. But with both of us working we knew we'd get by. What could discourage us, bursting with youth and strength (Chick was twenty-two; I twenty-one)?

Meantime, as a member of the executive training squad, I had become a department store salesclerk. Though I shared a flat with collegemates, I spent most week ends with my family in Montclair, New Jersey. "Don't you feel silly in that ball of wool?" the Gilbreth girls would ask as I appeared completely hidden in a cloche. "And are they really wearing bangs now and waists down to your knees?"

"It's the very latest fashion," I'd say, "even though you might not guess it here in the country."

"Here in the country, Ernie, we like attention without horselaughs. Doesn't belonging to this big family make us conspicuous enough already?"

Though my older sister Anne was married and Mart and Frank were in college, the other seven of us still lived in our rambling old house. Whenever I spoke about Chick, they looked worried one minute and hopeful the next. Fearful that he might not meet their rigid standards, praying that he would, they kept asking, "What's he like?"

"He's the cats."

"Handsome?"

"No. But darling. With oodles of personality."

"How old?"

"Old enough. Just right."

"You've said that before . . . and look at the sad apples we've had to toss out of here."

"But this time, honestly . . . this time . . ."

"If he's so perfect, let's look him over. When are we going to meet your big hero?"

"Never, if you go on like this. That's one reason why I decided to live in New York. . . ."

Eventually I accepted the fact that Chick should get

acquainted with my family. But he didn't welcome the suggestion. Somewhere, certainly not from me, he had heard tales of former suitors receiving the fire-and-ice treatment. "Can't this wait a while, honey?" he'd plead.

It is a fact that hesitation, like an Indian smoke signal, demands respect. "We'll wait of course," I said. "But shouldn't Mother come into our confidence immediately? She's a widow, you know, with tremendous home and business responsibilities. . . ."

As Chick still seemed undecided I added, "When Dad died five years ago, Mother became president of his time-and-motion-saving firm. She didn't have much choice, I guess, with eleven kids to raise and send through college."

He blinked.

"She's sure to be understanding about us, Chick. It wouldn't be fair to keep it a secret."

"I agree. But . . . well . . . could she meet us in New York maybe?"

"Of course. She's here on business almost every day."

He sighed gustily. "Make the date then . . . the sooner the better. But I wish we didn't have to go through these complications, darn it."

Several nights later the three of us met for dinner. Soon Chick was speaking of his younger brother and his childhood in Wellesley Hills, Massachusetts. A year after graduation from high school, when his father had married again, he had come here. As a salesman of heating installations, his salary was small. But if he could build business in the Bronx territory, he knew he could handle customers anywhere.

Mother kept listening, rubbing her finger along the tablecloth the way she does sometimes. When he had finished dessert she asked, "Won't you come for dinner soon, Charles?"

"Well . . . er . . . Mrs. Gilbreth . . ." Grinning, he didn't need to say any more.

"I know. But it may be easier than you expect. . . . Perhaps you'd enjoy an old-fashioned New England . . ."

His eyes began to shine.

"Do you like Deep Dish Apple Brown Betty?"

"You bet I do." All his reservations vanished. "I even dream about home cooking sometimes."

"Fine. Can we plan on this week end then?"

Now Chick fingered the tablecloth. "Yes," he said after a long pause.

Instead of looking forward to his visit to Montclair, I began to dread it. How, I wondered, had we gotten into this kettle of chowder? There could be so many headaches and hazards. More than once in the past, my six brothers had hurried a beau on his way. They either delivered the scram treatment together or became overaffectionate, dogging the dear one's footsteps. Either way, they killed the aura of romance pitifully.

Oh no, I thought, wincing at the memory of Bill, the ringleader of mischief, hosing a white-flanneled caller. Oh no, recalling six pained smiles one afternoon silently suggesting, "Take this sister off our hands, fellow. There are plenty more in our harem here." Willfully, was I to endure this again now? No. Oh no.

But at twenty-one, who can stay in despondency for more than a minute? Oh well, I told myself, we'll climb through this somehow. I hope.

"Stay in the background, everyone, please," I begged as the Gilbreth reception committee gathered on Sunday. "Let me answer the front door. And no embarrassing kissing noises."

In spite of these entreaties, Bobby and his collie were the first to welcome our guest. Stretching on tiptoe, our youngest brother shook hands gravely. "Hi, Charlie. Will you marry Ernestine, please?"

Several steps away, I stood stricken.

"If she can't cook, sport, the answer is NO." After disentangling himself from Pal's leaping paws, Chick came forward and kissed me. "Hello, honey. Now I've met one of the dozen, bring on the rest."

But they were already surrounding him and taking his coat with elaborate politeness.

In deference to my supersensitiveness, Mother had

made every effort to beautify the dining table. (How lovely, I thought, admiring the best banquet cloth, china and silver.) Having set our guest at her right, she kept filling his plate. "Are you ready for corned beef, Charles? Or a bit of turnip?"

Yet several yards away, mischief seemed to be brewing. Anyone could see that Bill and the knee-knickered brigade were flying danger signals: grins effaced into an expression of utter goodness, jabs into the next set of ribs, whispering and smothered giggles.

As we sisters removed the main-course plates, the conversation seemed harmless enough though: major-league batting averages, football arguments and side bets against unbeaten East Orange. Chick had admitted that baseball was his supreme delight and that he had pitched for the Wellesley High School team.

"You play lefty too?" the boys demanded in a hush of respect. "And Ern never dropped the slightest hint?"

I could imagine what this development would mean: a neighborhood game on the side lawn, continuing until after dark.

"Today, we've planned a special dessert for Charles," Mother said, after glancing toward the pantry. "I'm sure it will be delicious."

Everyone hushed as fifteen-year-old Lillian appeared with a mountain of steam in her arms. The smell of apples baked with lemon, sugar, butter and spice made us lick our lips. "Mmmmm, Brown Betty, our favorite favorite."

"It's an old family recipe," Mother said while Chick gloated. "A part of our New England heritage too."

Pal barked approvingly from under the table. And little Janey, on Mother's left, clapped her hands. "He's saying he likes it too. Hear him?"

"Of course we hear him," Bill said. "Even people in New York City can't miss Pal when he speaks."

"They hear you too, Brass Lungs," Bob said, leaning down to stroke his pet.

"Please, children," Mother said, putting her finger to her lips.

Lill came dancing from the pantry again. "Imagine. I almost forgot the butter sauce." She set it in the middle of the table.

"It's the sass that makes the pudding," Chick said in a tone reminiscent of the Pilgrim Fathers.

"So be it, you sassy thing," Bill grinned. "You'd moan plenty, wouldn't you, Carey, if you missed a shot at that sweet stuff?"

"You bet I would."

"Get ready to moan then."

While she was serving, Mother liked to ignore nonsense like this from the boys. Occasionally she'd frown slightly or shake her head. But since her sons claimed that yards of damask separated her from them during meals, it was hard to catch these signals. In any case, their best ideas often evolved in a flash second.

When Mother had heaped each plate with pudding, we passed it toward the right in basketball sequence. Consequently Jane was the first to help herself to sauce, as the boys had figured she would be.

As the bowl moved into the midst of the Gilbreth brotherhood, it disappeared. Having observed it one moment and missed it the next, Chick was confounded. Like a hound on the hunt, he looked sorrowfully from face to face and from fork to fork.

Meantime Mother had noticed his untouched plate. "You're waiting for sauce, aren't you, Charles? Will you pass it, children, please?"

A smothered guffaw came from the other end of the table.

"Come." Mother's voice was crisper now. "Let's show some consideration, boys."

"It's the sass that makes the pudding," someone intoned.

Tantalized, we began to investigate together. "Let's see. . . . Lill put the dish on the table. Jane, Bob, Fred, Bill and Dan served themselves, didn't they?"

Dan, a smaller edition of Bill, with the same love for mischief, flushed and choked. At the same moment Pal came scrambling from under his chair. "You've hidden it somewhere, funny boy," we cried. "Don't try to deny it."

After diving toward his feet, Dan brought up the empty bowl. "Sorry, folks. I did this for laughs. But Bob's dear old mutt . . ."

"Pal loves desserts," Janey said.

"Best eater in the family," Bob agreed. "Especially sweet stuff."

"Honestly, Dan," I said. "Sometimes I'm surprised at you."

When we had made a new batch of sauce, Chick took several spoonfuls. "This is perfect," he said happily. "I'd like to swim in it."

Mother was beaming too. "Do plan to come often, Charles."

"I will," he promised. "Every week end if you'll let me."

Later that afternoon, while the boys played baseball, Mother and I talked wedding plans. "We'll be married in the garden; it's so pretty in September."

"That spot by the rose arbor should be lovely, dear."

From the side lawn, male voices kept howling together. "Swing, Carey, you left-handed pull-hitter. Run, big boy, run."

"Just listen to them," I groaned. "Brothers kill romance dead as a duck, don't they?"

Mother patted my hand gently. "For the moment, perhaps. But you know the boys love you . . . and Charles too now."

"That's just the trouble. They love us too much. It's hard on an engaged girl."

"Nothing is perfect, Ernie. You mustn't expect it to be."

"So far you're right," I said.

CHAPTER 2

Bridegroom in Distress

THE next months flew by with Chick continuing to come to Montclair for week ends. Even on rainy days he'd be outside playing ball with my brothers. "Are you going to marry the six of them or me?" I'd ask, trying to smile.

He'd whack me over the shoulders. "Come on, honey. Get a glove. We can use you in left field."

Left field indeed! Wasn't I there already, please? In movies or romantic novels the hero was never so unfeeling. Nor did he wear the same beat-up jersey and sneakers Sunday after Sunday.

Since Mother was aware of these frustrations, she kept trying to divert me with wedding plans. "Shall we follow the pattern Anne set and invite just relatives and . . . ?"

"I guess so."

"Would you like President Thomas of Rutgers to serve as minister? He's an old family friend, you know. And the Stewart sisters could handle the music."

All this seemed fine. Dr. Thomas would add the touch of dignity which we could use always. And our young neighbors rendering *Lohengrin* via piano, violin and harp would be nice. Mother's bridal outfit could be hauled down from the attic and worn by another daughter. Yes. Yes. Why not?

"Then everything's settled, dear," Mother said gaily, ignoring my wandering attention. "This way, we'll avoid last-minute confusion."

"Thank goodness," I said, remembering Andie's wedding and near hysterics. "I'll be the calmest bride ever in this family . . . even if the boys use up the bath water again. Chick and I will be Rocks of Gibraltar."

After a quizzical look, Mother pursed her lips.

If Chick and I were absent-minded during our engagement, we had reasons beyond the usual ones. Both of us had assumed greater business responsibilities, he with a wider territory, I as an assistant buyer. Though there was no raise in salaries during these depression times, this didn't seem to matter.

Because each day drained our energy, we postponed facing personal problems. Getting married might mean budgeting, finding an apartment and shopping furniture. Only not now. We'd get to all this later.

We had agreed that we wished to be different from most betrothed couples; less dull. We intended to stay debonnaire. The devil with humdrum details.

In spite of our wish to be unique individuals, my platinum solitaire carried no distinctive features. But Chick presented it in his own way. "Here, honey," he said, slipping something cool and sparkling on my finger. "Now it's official."

I was in the kitchen shared with collegemates. I was frying a particularly lively fish. And now it was official.

"Why did you choose that awful moment?" I asked later.

"I figured if I could love you then, I'd love you always. Anyhow, once the ring was in my pocket, I couldn't wait."

Yet occasionally Chick's New England ancestry rose in him shouting. Soon after our job promotions, I persuaded him to meet me at the store one evening. Ill luck pulled me away from my department at the last minute. And I forgot to tell the clerks that Mr. Carey was due.

Later I found him snorting with irritation. "Don't suggest I come here again ever. I'd rather stand on Broadway in my bare skin."

"Why? What happened?"

"When I asked for you, the girls killed me with kindness. Holy Jehoshaphat." He made a mincing imitation. " 'She'll be back in a jiffy, Mr. Gilbreth.' Did you hear that, Ernie? They called me Mr. Gilbreth."

"You don't have to shout. Must you put on a scene here . . . just because . . . ?"

"Scene? Why wouldn't I blow up over this?" He swallowed painfully.

We stood facing each other miserably until one of the clerks passed. "Miss Gilbreth, he looks so much like you, we thought he was your brother. But now . . . well . . . we know he isn't."

"Excuse accepted this time, Ernie," Chick said afterwards. "But no one's going to jackass me soon again. Work at your job if you must. But don't remind me of it after hours."

"I'm sorry, darling."

"Once we're married you're going to be one person and only one person: Mrs. Charles Everett Carey. And if you don't like the idea, say so now."

Two weeks before the wedding, we faced the necessity of finding an apartment immediately. "I always thought this would be a lark," I said as we tramped through one building after another. "I never guessed rents were so high or stairs so steep."

"Let's look at a couple more places and call it quits. I'm ready to take the next hole with four walls and a floor."

Finally he signed a lease for a single-room-kitchen-bath combination on West Seventeenth Street. "It's pretty dark and airless," Chick said, brooding at the courtyard below, "but we'll be here mostly at night. And we'll sleep better if our bills are paid."

On Monday we returned to our jobs, aglow with a sense of accomplishment. Five of six pieces of furniture had been ordered and Mother was giving us curtains, bedding and kitchen equipment. So we seemed to be set.

Yet other matters began to demand attention even though we fought them. Enjoying the delay routine in ourselves, we failed to appreciate it in each other. This was clear one day at lunch, shortly before our marriage.

Chick had urged me to assemble a warm wardrobe for our honeymoon in New Hampshire. Detesting such gear, I groaned.

"I'm serious, Ern. No foolish fripperies or you'll freeze to death."

"But I loathe scratchy clothes. There's been no time yet for thinking about a trousseau."

"With just four days left, how can you twiddle your thumbs?"

"We're in our busy season getting set for Christmas. I'll be up to my ears at the store till the night before our wedding."

"Your job makes too many demands. There'll be a comeuppance some day." He reeled suddenly. "Listen to me taking you over the coals. Golly . . ."

"Now what?"

"Ho. Ho. Imagine. I haven't ordered my bridal trousers yet. Forgot them completely."

"Ordered? Where do you get those millionaire ideas? Aren't ready-made white flannels good enough?"

"Of course not. With my long legs and build do you ant me to look like an ape boy?"

"Dear, how could you be so careless, waiting until now?"

"Well . . . er . . ."

"Suppose the tailor is busy? Suppose he can't finish anything in time?"

"He won't let me down."

"He could. He might."

"Indeed he won't. Let's finish up here and I'll see him immediately." Chick began to chuckle.

I knew he was imagining himself at the altar with shanks pink as a baby's. It was an entrancing picture and I had to smile too.

Now our big day, September the thirteenth, had come at last. The house in Montclair tingled with excitement, preparations and laughter. And the basket of chrysanthemums in the front hall seemed to shout: We're having a wedding today.

Whatever sunshine streamed among us, we were making ourselves this morning. For rain had come unexpectedly, canceling the garden ceremony. "Still," as Mother said at breakfast, "what do we care really? The side porch can be transformed with candelabra and banks of flowers. And it isn't the first time guests have stood shoulder to shoulder here."

Not the first time nor the last, I thought, remembering occasions when our downstairs had been filled to capacity: christenings, teas, high-school dances with people everywhere.

Though we women stayed philosophical, the boys were inconsolable. "What a shame," Chick said as water swam down the windowpanes. "I'd been counting on one last play-off."

"Is this your only worry, honey?"

"Sure. What else . . . except my wedding trousers maybe?"

"They're coming later, aren't they?"

"Good old Jake and Ted promised to bring them by three-thirty. They may celebrate a bit on the way out; but they won't fail me. Now run on upstairs. Rest. Relax. Do whatever a bride does. Oh golly, look at that infernal rain."

Who can understand men? I thought. Don't they ever grow up?

Until midafternoon we Gilbreth sisters hemmed, pressed and packed my wardrobe. "I love you, Ernie," Anne said as we finished, "but why did you get in this jam-up at the last minute? Taking care of a husband and two children is *simple* compared to this. I'm exhausted."

"Doesn't the matron of honor like helping the bride?"

"Ye . . . es. Of course. But this time I had hoped for a nice leisurely bath before we dressed."

"Me too," I groaned.

While working, we had heard the boys splashing and howling in the bathrooms. "I'll get in line ahead of you girls," Martha said, closing a suitcase, "because I'm helping Mother greet the guests today. Besides, one of us three older daughters should look presentable."

"Save a little hot water for us," we pleaded.

Later Anne and I emerged from our showers, shivering and furious. "Greenland as usual," she wailed. "I'm ice from the neck down."

"It's tradition, isn't it? Brrr."

While we finished dressing, Mother, Martha, Lillian and Jane welcomed the musicians. As guests began to arrive, we heard Chick, the Gilbreth boys and Pal cavorting in the boys' wing. Then we caught the hum of string tuning and conversation downstairs.

"I must be jittery," Anne said, making wild swipes at her hair. "Isn't it silly?"

"Very," I whispered, trying to control my shaking fingers.

Dressed and groomed at last, we surveyed each other joyfully. Anne's hair and eyes were shining above her chalk-blue costume. Then I caught a flash of myself in the mirror: a radiant new person decked in Chantilly lace.

Frank, eldest of the Gilbreth brotherhood, came

through the doorway with Pal at his heels. "Hey, you girls look good." Lunging, our college sophomore made a frantic grab. "Down, boy, down."

"Hi, handsome," I caroled, "aren't you slicked up like a sheik today. All set to give me away?"

"You bet. Biggest bang of my life. I can't wait." He continued to grapple with Pal. "Say, Anne, what shall we do with this baboon? Chain him somewhere?"

"Chloroform him with my compliments. So far he's wrecked seven pairs of stockings."

"Tie him down cellar," I said, "and padlock the door."

"O.K. I hope Bob leaves him there. Otherwise almost anything can happen."

Soon Frank returned, frowning. "You should hear that pest howling his lungs out. It will murder the bridal music."

"Maybe that will be a blessing," Anne said as the Stewart sisters kept tuning their instruments loudly.

Frank grinned at me. "Say, Ern, I've been stalling . . . trying not to tell you . . . but Chick's in a pickle."

"Wouldn't you expect him to be?"

"You see, his white flannels haven't come yet." He grinned harder than ever.

"All right, you jokester," I said. "I'm dying laughing."

"We're getting worried, girls. We don't know where to turn next."

"Ho. Ho. What a clown. How did you dream up this yack-yack?"

After observing him thoughtfully, Anne glanced at her watch. "The ceremony starts in ten minutes, doesn't it?"

Was my matron of honor in on this gag too?

"Stop it," I cried. "It's no time for teasing."

"Look," Frank said, "wake up, Ernie, for goodness' sakes. I'm serious. Chick's running round and round in his shorts. Bill and I have tried everywhere to find some pants that will fit. But that guy you picked is all legs like a grasshopper."

"Go on," I said, beginning to believe him at last.

"My pants are too wide. Bill's are too short. Chick's father's are too big. His brother's are too small. Now we're hauling the men guests upstairs one by one. But it's the same old story."

"Does Mother know about this?" Anne asked.

"Sure. She's taking it in stride of course. She's told the trio to keep playing their stuff over and over." Frank sat down on the bed and sighed.

I threw myself down beside him.

"Chick's the saddest guy you've ever seen. In between howls he keeps shaking hands. 'Hello, how are you,' with some stranger offering his trousers. Next he's right back in his underwear again. 'Nice to have met you.' " He gulped back a guffaw.

"Don't you dare laugh," I cried. "Or I'll kill you."

"Poor Ernie,"Anne said.

"You mean poor Chick," Frank insisted, still fighting to look serious. "He's aged fifty years. Ho. Ho. Ho."

"And our poor guests," I said. "How will they take this delay?"

"They can't walk out now, can they?" Frank cocked his head toward the door and grimaced. "If that trio doesn't play something besides 'I Love You Truly' for the seventeenth time, I'll go nuts."

"How about me?" Jumping to my feet, I began to pace back and forth.

"Cut that Highland Fling and take it easy," Frank said. "We'll work this out somehow."

"Chick's friends will be here any minute," Anne said, putting her arm around my waist. "They know he can't be married without his trousers."

Frank chuckled. "In a pinch, he can wear his baseball outfit to the altar. Well, I'll go back and hold his hand again. Buck up, girls."

While the next minutes dragged on, we listened to "I Love You Truly," "Love's Old Sweet Song" and the "Indian Love Call" rendered with variations. Each composition was followed by a roar of voices from the boys' wing. "Pants here yet? Are Chick's pants here?"

"Keep calm, Ernie," Anne said as I kept dancing. "Five years from now you'll smile at this."

"I won't either."

Half an hour later, Martha came flying past us. "Eureka, folks. *THEY'RE* here at last. Let's get going."

In a flash the bridal procession formed at the top of the stairs. With Andie directly ahead and Frank towering at my side, everything became all right.

Bob's voice and a sudden burst of barking formed a duet close by. "Who put Pal in the cellar? He wants to see the wedding, don't you, boy?"

"Hang on to that animal," we warned. "Tie him. Choke him. Drown him. He's the very last straw."

"I've got him by his collar. Don't worry."

As the first chords of *Lohengrin* boomed, Janey, our flower girl, gave a frantic signal. "One . . . two . . . three . . . start."

"Which foot first?" Anne asked in a whisper. "Left or right?"

"Either or both," I answered. "What does it matter, dear God?"

Frank had tucked the bride's hand in his. "Don't laugh at the wrong time, Ernie, do you hear? *Do you hear?* This is a serious business . . . a serious business . . . a serious business."

We were walking down one step, then the next. We were in the main hall facing guests, familiar, strange, smiling, serious. We were in the living room with more guests.

Now came the moment when Frank and I blundered toward the harp, a mass of twanging, dangerous goldness.

Catching ourselves, we veered sharply, fought the urge to snicker. Finally we reached the porch, the bridal bower and our man from Rutgers waiting to perform the ceremony.

The groom in his blue coat and blessed trousers stepped toward the bride. "I Charles take thee Ernestine . . . and thereto I plight my troth.". . . "I Ernestine take thee Charles . . ." . . . "Then I pronounce that they are man and wife."

Everything will be fine, I thought. We'll have our ups and downs maybe but it won't be dull.

A kiss now, while Mother smiled and the young Gilbreths fought their giggles. Off in the distance Pal barked approvingly. Then Chick was whispering in my ear, "I won't go through this razzle-dazzle again . . . ever. Once is enough, Mrs. Carey."

"Isn't it," I said, squeezing his hand.

CHAPTER 3

Baked Beans for the Bride

ANY apartment, I suppose, would have seemed perfect that first year together. This one in the off-beat garage-warehouse district may have had some blemishes. Yet nothing could disillusion Chick and me; not even a friend's caustic "It's fine, kids. But why pick a place in the slums?"

For many reasons our West Seventeenth neighborhood didn't encourage walking alone in the dark. But our home boasted a fireplace and cost only one week's combined salary per month. Though it may have had too many doors and too few windows, this never seemed to matter.

As joint jobholders with no domestic help, we needed only a small, simple setup. Extra space and furniture, we knew, would mean extra chores. This way, we hoped to be free as birds.

At my request, Mother had redesigned and equipped the kitchen as a wedding present. Work surfaces had been adjusted to our heights for minimum bending and reaching. Hooks had been placed with an eye to Chick's left-handedness. A stool on wheels meant that I could sit while I peeled potatoes after a strenuous day (the wheels providing easy ambulation from table to icebox to sink). Four lines of verse in Mother's handwriting bore the title "Our Teamwork Kitchen" and hung near the stove. Two aprons, one butcher style, one small and frilly, dangled from the door.

These double aprons, more than anything else, amused our friends; especially since mine was the only one used for several weeks. "Good Lord, are you supposed to work here too?" Chick's chums asked in alarm.

"That's the general idea," he'd blush a little. "Only so far, I ain't."

They'd turn to me then. "You mean you'd welcome that hulking ham's assistance?"

"Why not? When I drag home at night, two extra hands and feet would be heavenly."

After examining Chick again, they'd snort with appreciation. "Imagine Carey bending over a hot stove or making a pie. In that butcher's outfit too. Humph."

Chick's face would turn purple. "Honestly, Ern," he'd say afterwards. "Burn that blasted apron, will you? I can swallow everything, including that poetry motto. But I wouldn't be caught dead in that chef outfit."

"Maybe you'll use it some day instead of sitting around in that smoking jacket eternally. I need a little help here. Really I do."

"Sorry, honey. The kitchen's your bailiwick; not mine."

"But this is 1930; not 1910."

"I'm still a man; and you're still a woman . . . thank heaven."

Moments like these were forgotten in the thrill and newness of being together. And I was never sure what Chick would do next. For example, as I came into the apartment one evening, he leaped from a closet with a shout. "Yoo-hoo, baby."

For a moment I couldn't identify this blond cyclone in shirt sleeves. Then I gasped, "Did you want to scare me pink, for goodness' sakes?"

"Of course not. But I thought you'd prefer this to the old peck-on-the-cheek routine." He did a clog step. "Just because we're married, we don't have to be graybeards, do we?"

Afterwards, when I had finished the supper dishes, he found some music on the radio. "May I have this next dance, please, Mrs. Carey? You look ravishing tonight."

We swooped, galloped and slid through elaborate steps together. "Honestly, Chick," I said, tucking my chin into his shoulder, "you're the best dancer I know anywhere. How did you get that way?"

"I don't know, honey. And no one ever told me that before. You're not so bad yourself; really light as a feather."

"Did you have dozens of girls before you met me?"

"Just one or two — here and there. Nothing serious. How about you?"

"Nothing ever before like this."

"Good God, I should hope *not*. Come on, Ernie. Let's try this new step. We stand arm and arm *so* . . . and walk forward . . . one . . . two . . . three. Then we come together this way, with a little jump."

"Where did you learn that hot number?"

"Why do you care?"

"Because, Chick, I understand the chorus in Sandy's Night Club is featuring it now."

"But I haven't been there for at least a year. How do you know so much about it anyway?"

"Well . . . it happens that before I met you . . ."

Seriously offended, we jarred to a halt. "Why, you two-timing little double-talker . . ." . . . "You no-good Casanova, painting yourself as dear old Faithful."

"Ho. Here you kept me dancing on my toes and swallowing that girl-from-the-country line. . . ."

"But listen, Chick."

"I will not. You listen to me, young lady."

Pausing for breath, we stood glaring and ignoring loud thumps on the door. "Hey, you, what's going on here . . . hippopotamuses or something? *Can* that noise. Downstairs the plaster's coming off our ceiling."

"Sorry," we said. "Awfully sorry."

"Come on, honey," Chick said impulsively, grabbing

my hand. "One last swing-around; then we'll stop. Step, step, step; come together; jump."

"Fred Astaire has nothing on you," I sighed as we finished. "Honestly."

"Thanks, Mrs. Carey. You'll do too . . . in a pinch."

But soon, of course, our disagreements touched deeper and more sensitive spots. Mainly, because Chick holds strong opinions on all matters, including art and music. It is a fact that my taste in paintings, drawings and sculpture is unpredictable. Unblessed with a fine ear, I would rather read about opera than hear it blasting from a sound box or pair of human lungs.

Since we owned only one pint-sized radio in those days, Chick's passion for noise was not the problem that it has been since. But we argued plenty over "what is art; what is beautiful."

During the holiday in Europe two summers before, I had collected several souvenirs. The most precious was a seventeenth-century print of a gentleman reclining in a chair. For some reason the artist failed to include his subject's upper thighs and buttocks. Consequently, the effect is dreamy.

On our first date together, I had shown this masterpiece to Chick. "Isn't it unique? Isn't it lovely?"

"Yes. If you like it."

"But don't *you* like it?"

"If you like it, Ernie, I like it."

This had to satisfy me.

When Christmas came, I decided to give my betrothed the one object which meant a deep personal sacrifice. With more pain than joy, I removed my picture from the wall, wrapped and presented it.

"Well, I'll be a monkey's hind leg," he said, making no secret of his amazement. "So this belongs to me now? You're much too generous."

After we were married, though, he was less careful of my feelings. We were hanging pictures at the time. And I had insisted that "The Seatless One" be placed where we could enjoy him.

"*Must* we?"

"Why not?"

"He's a sorry character. I've never liked him."

Tears came to my eyes.

"All right, honey. All right. Have it your way. Only a man minus his behind doesn't belong in my ball club."

With this impasse behind us, we hung the rest of our prints, etchings, woodcuts and watercolors. "This stuff is really good," Chick crowed, whamming the last hook into place. "These artists kept their minds on their jobs."

I had been unpacking a carton of decorative objects. Humming radiantly, I placed a tall, gaunt figure on the table. "Isn't the best spot for him *here?*"

Perhaps I should have anticipated a second argument on this treasure. Months before marriage, Chick had taken an immediate dislike to my crimson-mantled Mephistopheles. "Why do you keep this Schoolgirl's Nightmare, Ern? I hate the sight of that leering, sneering, jeering jerk. Even Goethe wouldn't give him house room."

"Your lack of taste matches your lack of tact," I said, bitterly hurt.

"Why attach yourself to such a horror?"

"Because he's glorious, that's why. Because he expresses a sort of mood. Also because he is a rare bargain which I bought in Holland for two dollars."

"You wasted two bucks then. Look at those clawlike hands. Ugh!"

After this, whenever Chick came to call, he'd drop Mephistopheles into the nearest wastebasket. Then I'd rush to rescue my beloved and wonder why men are so heartless.

Now that the Schoolgirl's Nightmare had come to board with us, the issue rose like a geyser again. "If this spot on the table isn't right," I said, "suppose you suggest a better place."

"With pleasure." After setting down his hammer, Chick grabbed the little statue and dived into the kitchen. He returned empty-handed.

"All right," I fumed. "Where did you put him?"

"In the garbage pail."

Two weeks later Mephistopheles wound up there permanently. Chick had blundered into the table, smashing him to bits. "I'll admit I was clumsy," he said gleefully, "but don't expect me to be sorry."

Chick had brought several precious possessions into our home too. Least of all, I liked the baseball which he had caught years before in Fenway Park. Though it was grimy and beginning to peel and smell, he kept it on top of our bureau. "Reminds me of that terrific Red Sox-Yankee game," he'd say, deaf to my objections. "I was there with Dad that day."

Above the ball and tucked into the base of our only good mirror was another memento: a dog-eared photograph of the 1925 Wellesley High School first stringers in Rover Boy uniforms. "There's Eddie, our catcher, Ern, . . . and Dave . . . and that embryonic string bean in the center is guess who? Me."

"Mercy, you look like babies," I'd say, moved by the innocence of their faces. "I bet none of you shaved in those days."

"Sure we did. Twice a week at least." He'd smooth the picture fondly.

"Must we keep this here, blocking half the mirror?" I'd ask. "Can't we frame it and hang it somewhere else?"

"Well . . . yes . . . if we ever find time."

Since we never did find time, the photograph stayed where it was, guillotining my reflection. Fie, fie, boys, I'd think again and again. You're cutting me to the quick.

Chick's collection of pipes seemed manly and right, even though they smelled fearfully sometimes. But I loathed the smoking jacket he wore every evening. Since it seemed to smack of bachelor-apartment sophistication, I concluded that it was a gift from a former sweetheart. (Years later, when I confessed this hunch to Chick, he could scarcely believe it. "You silly child, I bought that extravagance with my very first pay check. That's why it means so much to me still.")

Though I have always worried about fires, Chick's smoking habits included using a cardboard wastebasket as an ash tray. Ensconced in his jacket and favorite chair, he'd dump live coals there repeatedly. "Some day you'll burn up everything we own," I'd warn.

"When I do, you can blast the daylights out of me. But until then, stop jittering, will you?"

"But it's taking such foolish chances, honey."

"Not when I concentrate on being careful."

But this was minor compared to other matters. When a boy from New England marries a New York working girl, the adjustment can be big. Different roots stretch out in different directions; and it's not rib-tickling.

During our engagement perhaps Chick was blind to my limitations. Or he may have overlooked the fact that my only homemaking qualifications were energy and a buoyant heart. To compensate, I've kept busy with a business career, reading and writing; just as an opium addict turns to his pipe.

If Chick's mother had been alive and close by during the first year of our marriage, she might have eased many of our misunderstandings. Instead Chick kept aching for the comforts of his childhood: home-cooked pastry, spotless housekeeping, hand-and-foot service. Though he expected his bride to re-create this Paradise immediately, I simply couldn't.

"Good Lord, honey," he'd wail, waiting for his dinner. "Aren't we ever going to eat?"

"I'm hurrying, but I've been home only twenty minutes."

He'd sit puffing his pipe. "I'm starved. Why don't you quit or get a job with decent hours?"

I'd continue clattering a spoon at triple speed.

"Holy mackerel," he hollered one night. "You put a subway to shame with that racket. How can I read my paper?"

With apron flaring, I rushed from the kitchen. "Sit there, you oaf. Complain like an emaciated Buddha."

"Who wouldn't look emaciated on your cooking?"

"Did you marry me for my cooking? Did you?"

"All right. So I didn't." After pulling me down on his lap, he wiggled my chin. "I love you, dear; but I just can't stand this bilge-water diet. We're economizing too much maybe."

I leaped to my feet. "Bilge water indeed, you wretch."

"I need red meat, Ernie. If you dish out one more slice of liverwurst or hash . . ."

"But red meat costs money. It takes time to cook. We have limited money and time."

"And limited digestions too. A grade-F boardinghouse would be better than this."

"You're the most tactless . . ."

"I'm not either. I'm just plain hungry."

Another time my exasperated cries from the kitchen brought him running. I was creaming fish and the sauce had lumped.

"Gas shouldn't be on full tilt," he said, extinguishing it. "And you've used too much flour." His nose wrinkled. "Of course in the old days only our *cats* ate tuna. But when Mother fixed turkey . . ." He smacked his lips in ecstasy.

I kept fighting the glutinous mass in our double boiler. "Tell me more. I long to hear about your blessed mother's housekeeping and cooking. Did she garnish everything with mushrooms?"

"Sure. It would make your mouth water."

I added some canned milk to my mixture.

"She'd cook them fresh from the fields in lots of butter. Delicious."

"Until they sizzled and popped?"

"Heavens no. Gently . . . ge . . . ntly . . . until they were tender. Mmmm."

"Your mother never measured anything, did she?"

"Of course not. Cooking came naturally. With a flick of her wrist, she'd whip up Parker House rolls, doughnuts, apple pies." He rubbed his stomach like a small boy.

"I do the best I can, Chick. But I'll never please you. Never."

"You will too, dear."

"I need help."

"Then I'll help you."

"By not talking about Parker House rolls and pies?"

"Yes. But I mean really help. Two nights from now will be Saturday, won't it? Listen . . . I'm going to cook us the best New England supper you ever ate. Let's see. . . . We'll need a couple of quarts of pea beans, salt pork, molasses, and stuff for coleslaw. Boy oh boy."

Reaching up, I hugged him hard. "You're so sweet. And I'm so lucky. But you've taken on a load of work."

"Nonsense. Who's afraid of kid stuff like this? Just watch Carey, the gourmet, produce a masterpiece."

"Thank you. Thank you."

On Saturday night, I returned from work later than usual. Whew, I thought, sniffing smoke in our corridor, some neighbor must be burning sneakers or worse.

As I entered our apartment, the windows were open and the kitchen door was tightly closed. Then as a crackling noise grew louder, I saw the wastebasket in flames. "Fire, Chick, fire," I shouted. "Come quick."

"There's nothing to worry about. I spilled something on the stove."

"Get a pail. Hurry." Banging open the door, I shook him. "This is serious, really."

"All right," he said when the excitement was over. "I'll be more careful next time; now I've learned a lesson. . . . Sit down in that easy chair and relax. Don't dare come near the kitchen."

After waiting endlessly, I had endured more than enough. "Holy smoke, Chick. Aren't we ever going to eat?"

He crashed through the doorway, his hair on end. "How can you twiddle your fingers and complain? What do you suppose I've been doing all day?"

"Why don't you quit or get a job with decent hours? I'm starved."

He pulled me up into his arms. "Did you marry me for my cooking? Did you?" Then as I shook my head, "The stove is a sight, honey. I'm sorry."

I put on my apron. "Let's see. Where shall we start?"

"Heaven only knows."

Murder, I thought, looking around the kitchen. An earthquake must have hit us. Whew.

After dinner we did the dishes together for the first time. "From now on I'm going to help you," Chick said, wiping a glass furiously. "This job isn't the snap I thought it would be."

"Dinner was perfect," I said, swabbing a plate. "Let's have beans every Saturday, shall we?"

"Why not?"

"That coleslaw is delicious. I could eat it forever."

"We're going to," he said, grimacing at a giant bowl, "unless you'd rather roll in the stuff."

CHAPTER 4

Welcome to Washington Square

AFTER a year at West Seventeenth Street, we moved to an apartment on Washington Square. Reviewing this new neighborhood with its park and stately buildings, we knew we had come from rags to riches. "We worked hard for this," Chick said joyfully. "I wouldn't change places even with Charlie Schwab."

Though this home was smaller than the previous one, it offered an outside view, air and sunshine. No lights-across-the-courtyard blinded us as we tried to sleep; no scraping ash cans woke us at dawn. Best of all, twin wall-beds, the last word in éclat, we thought, left space for a new sofa and console radio.

Even before we had hung our curtains, Carey's Castle became headquarters for our friends. Incessant gaiety was fine of course. But now and again, Chick yearned for his slippers while I ached to read or do a bit of writing. "What is this place, the Village hangout?" we'd ask as we dragged into bed.

Our most frequent visitors were Chick's old wedding-trousers buddies, Jake and Ted. They liked to say that his crisis had scared them from matrimony forever. "After seeing poor Carey pale, palpitating and pantless all illusions went to thunder."

When the boys had made the round of night clubs each evening, they'd bang on our door. "Wake up, sleepyheads. Come entertain us. Where are your manners?"

"We haven't any. Go away."

The pounding would continue until we switched on the light, fumbled into our bathrobes and made them welcome. "It's time you got up and scratched yourselves," they'd complain.

Hours later, after a session of bridge, poker or yat, we'd scramble some eggs. Finally we'd ask, "Haven't you a home somewhere? Don't you have to work tomorrow?"

"Let's see. Do I have a job still? Maybe so."

When Jake married a debutante and moved to Pittsburgh, I wasn't sorry. But he missed his cronies and returned to New York all too frequently. Then he and Ted would relive old times together and give us the rousing treatment.

While we sat yawning, Jake would boast about being a model husband. "You should see me pamper Gertrude with breakfast-in-bed. She loves it too." Next came the era when he described Jake, Jr., from the diaper stage up.

Since life in Greenwich Village didn't include breakfast-in-bed and babies, we weren't really interested. So whenever the opportunity arose, we switched the subject.

"Is this all you can think about?" Jake scoffed one night, after I had mentioned a Broadway show.

We looked at him blankly. "Why not? What's wrong, Uncle Hiram?"

"I hate to say it, but you're getting to be bird-brains."

"A good guy gone to the dogs," we said as he came less and less. "What a shame. What a waste."

Though Ted often had a girl in tow, it was never the same one twice. "Sure she's a doll," he'd say about Ginny, Toots or Midge. "But she'd be expensive. I want a woman tycoon — provided she can't outwrestle me."

His dates, of course, were anything but women tycoons. In contrast to Ted's broad Harvard accent, they always seemed to lisp and use "doncher-knows."

One late afternoon in our apartment we watched his downfall begin. Effie was a pint-sized Skidmore graduate, blessed with a listening ear. Redheaded and beautiful, she soon had Ted expanding like a rose. "I seldom talk about business but . . ."

By eight o'clock Chick managed to interrupt his monologue. "Look, folks. If we're going out to dinner tonight . . ."

"Come on, duck," Effie said, half closing her eyes and breathing deeply. "Let's get started."

"Where? Why?"

"It's time to eat."

"Eat? When we can talk, who wants to eat?"

"I do." She took his arm.

He dragged himself up from the sofa. "All right, sugar. If you insist."

She did insist . . . on blue points, artichoke, filet mignon and cherry jubilee. Thus began the courtship which continued for a year. They were married in the Little Church Around the Corner, with Chick as best man. "There goes the last of the Braves," he said almost tearfully that night. "Good old Ted went down fighting."

In addition to stag visitors, many young couples came frequently. Though many of them no longer lived in New York, they shared their Smith-College-Ivy-League reunions with us. "How do you get along with so little sleep?" they'd ask after an uproarious week end. "Where do you get the strength?"

We wondered ourselves, sometimes.

Our favorite guests were the Smileys from northern New Jersey. Like us, this lawyer-schoolteacher team had been forced to postpone a family. But Sue was a resourceful blonde and a born mother. Chick liked to say that she resembled us Gilbreths in her energy and love of small fry.

Soon after we had moved to the Square, Sue and her husband came to dinner. "Wait till you hear the big news. We're up to our ears in babies."

"In every size, shape, color and smell," Dave said testily.

"They're darlings," Sue said, rubbing her head against his shoulder. "Did you ever see anything sweeter, dear?" She turned to us radiantly. "We have puppies, kittens, bunnies, piglets and a goat who's expecting."

On later visits we could see that Sue's four-legged family gave her a new serenity. But Dave looked increasingly harried. "I've never liked goats; but I milk one every morning, damn it. I detest chickens. But we own a hundred at least."

"He'll adjust in time," Sue caroled.

But to date Dave hasn't adjusted. In addition to six children he's fathering four dogs, two sheep, a cow, innumerable cats, an aquarium of rare fish and a parakeet. "Gad," he groaned when we saw him recently. "They eat us out of house and home."

Another couple, who lived near Central Park, combined generosity with playfulness. On Easter, they gave us a beribboned live rabbit. "Greetings, Careys, good luck and good-by."

"If they left leprosy here, I couldn't feel worse," Chick said, failing to appreciate this gag.

"Have you forgotten the spirit behind the gift?" I teased.

For three miserable days we failed to house or dispose of our pet. "Believe me," Chick said, dumping him back into his crate for the hundredth time, "old Houdini is heading for hasenpfeffer."

Finally we presented a token of love to the milkman. "Take him, please. You're an angel."

A few months later, on Chick's birthday, the same friends gave him two kittens. "Happy days, Chickadee."

Chick's love of cats had begun in his boyhood. Whenever he met a Mr. or Mrs. Whiskers, he'd squat on his heels, communing with his friend. "Wuzza, wuzza. Pretty baby."

This scene always inspired nostalgic memories. "I grew up with two wonderful animals, Ern. Dad brought Nip and Tuck home in his pocket one night. They grew to be enormous and beautifully mannered."

Because Nip, Jr., and Tuck, Jr., filled a deep longing in Chick, I tried to like them. But cats have given me chills ever since one deposited a dead rat under my bed. "Isn't this a stroke of genius?" the worst-of-all-Gilbreth-pets yowled in the darkness, scaring me half to death. "Wake up, you lazy thing, and pin a blue ribbon on me."

Having come, our kittens decided to conquer everything and everybody. Mewing eternally, they pranced, climbed and cavorted wherever they pleased: over the sink, down the table legs, in and out, back and forth, round and round.

Though Chick housebroke his babies almost overnight,

their social behavior lacked finesse. When guests had settled themselves, the twin Juniors would scoot up trousers or under skirts without an ah, yes, or boo. "Cheeky, aren't they?" someone exclaimed once.

"Please forgive and forget," we'd say, blushing.

A favorite couple whom we saw repeatedly lived on our floor. Daphne worked at my store as a French Shop model. Her husband, Ashley Dodge, was a young instructor in the university. "We're a team," he'd tell us proudly, "just as you two are."

Chick believed that Daphne was an old-fashioned girl in modern clothes. In any case, she was a breathtaking brunette with skin like a Rubens painting.

Our friendship began one evening in a neighborhood restaurant. Afterwards it seemed almost as though the four of us were married to each other. "But we aren't, darn it," Chick would say sometimes.

Since I worshiped everything about "Daff," I tried to duplicate her lilting, queenly ways. One night I came home with an elaborate twin hairdo. "Hell and Maria, take off that wig," Chick said after astonished scrutiny. "Be yourself, little bright-eyes."

Having failed to become a second Daphne, I decided to enlist her help in beautifying our apartment. Handicapped by kittens or not, I wished to add charm, warmth and *savoir-faire.*

Soon we had our men in their shirt sleeves, moving a

chair here, the table there. "It's super-duper, girls," Chick said, impressed by the results, "and worth a little sweat."

As we finished rehanging the pictures one night, Daff's and my friendship almost went on the rocks. For her new eye-level arrangement had eliminated one small print. "Oh," I groaned, heartsick at the discovery. "Are you discarding my lovely little man?"

"You know he's nothing, dear, don't you?"

Chick was beaming approval.

"Look at him again, Ernie. Doesn't he lack something?" Then when I was too upset to answer, "Don't cry, honey. We'll put everything back as it was."

"No you don't," Chick cried, pounding his chest.

So we tucked my favorite picture away in the closet and forgot it for the next six years.

Chick's baseball buddies, however, stayed in our mirror. "How darling!" Daff cried, after inspecting them. "Is that cutie in the center you, Master Carey? No wonder Ernie keeps this here."

"We'll get it framed eventually," I promised.

When the Dodges entertained, they always did it superbly. Though Daphne worked long hours at the store, she was a relaxed and gifted hostess. "How do you do it?" I'd ask as she served a tasty meal on schedule.

"By fixing everything the night before, dear. It's easy."

After one of these dinners at the Dodges, Chick decided that we should "entertain" more often. "Why do you duck this sort of thing, Ern? It's simple and I'll help you gladly."

"But . . ." I kept saying, "and besides, with the cats . . ."

"Nonsense. What the Dodges can do, we Careys can do. Where's your courage?"

"Frankly, this scares me."

"Women who scare easily aren't worth a nickel. Now stop being a baby."

Finally, I agreed to have a small buffet supper. Several months before, we had been visitors at the Brooklyn home of Chick's district manager. Until now, I had postponed offering return hospitality. Even now, I trembled with dread.

"Why agitate?" Chick asked. "Ezra Thorpe and his wife are human. They'll like us the way we are."

"Will they?"

"Sure. Remember that all of us look pretty much the same in our underwear. Nobody's going to eat you, honey."

"Can't we take them out somewhere?"

"Of course not. It's nicer here."

But I wasn't convinced it was nicer or even sensible. Hadn't Mrs. Thorpe spoken continually of her married daughters' skills? "Home and family must come first. A girl owes it to her husband, I always say . . ." (Fair enough, but did she mean home and family or domestic duties possibly?)

Still, as Chick insisted, we had delayed hospitality too long. And there was no reason to go into a tailspin now.

Once the Thorpes and the Dodges had been invited for Saturday night, Daff was a source of strength. She'd come half an hour early, she said, to help in the kitchen. "Ashley and I love making parties click. Everyone will be buddy-buddy in no time."

"You darling," I cried, hugging her.

Our big evening came at last with inevitable crises. Though I had prepared what I could the night before, the butcher failed to deliver the chicken. Consequently it and the vegetables had to be fixed at the last minute.

"Hell's bells," Chick said as I hustled into my apron. "The Thorpes are due in half an hour. Will you ever be ready?"

"Oh dear. Oh dear. Where's the bread? Didn't I buy any, for goodness' sakes?"

"I'll borrow some from the Dodges."

"Hurry, please. Tell Daff I need her desperately."

"Ashley'll be here in a minute," Chick said as he thumped a loaf on the kitchen table. "But Daff's detained somewhere. I'm going to the corner for some cigarettes."

"Leave the door off the catch, will you? And put those infernal kittens in the bathroom. I've tripped over them fifty times."

When the buzzer rang a moment later, I was chopping celery. "Walk in, Ashley. Walk in. Stop being so doggone coy." Then as I lunged out to investigate, "Oh gracious. Good evening, Mr. and Mrs. Thorpe."

Though we shook hands warmly, I longed to drop through the floor. And when Chick returned, my cheeks were still blazing.

"We're early, of course," Mrs. Thorpe said, settling herself on the sofa. "But I always say, better early . . ."

Ashley arrived now, smiling and scholarly. But there was no sign of Daphne.

While the men talked together, we women grew better acquainted. "Imagine wanting us here tonight, after working all day," Mrs. Thorpe said kindly.

From the corner of my eye, I could see the chicken waiting on the kitchen table. Finally Mrs. Thorpe saw it too. "Let's get him in the oven, shall we?" She bustled into the kitchen. "You finish stuffing him, dear, while I string the beans. We'll be through in no time."

Gentle, beautiful, understanding woman, I thought. Can you guess how much I love you?

As we finished the salad she said, "This is a new day, isn't it . . . with husbands and wives sharing everything side by side?"

"But I'm not half what I'd like to be . . . at housekeeping especially."

"Who is, child?"

While everything was cooking, Chick fetched the kittens from the bathroom. "Wuzza, wuzza. Did Daddy lock you away, poor sings? Want to meet all the folks?" (Meow. Meow.) . . . "Here are our youngsters, friends, Nip, Jr., and Tuck, Jr."

"We love cats," Mrs. Thorpe said, as Tuck, Jr., careened across her bosom. "They add hominess, don't they?"

"We have only three," her husband added, flicking a whisker, "but I wish we had six."

When dinner was ready, Daphne arrived, newly coiffured and lacquered. "Excuse me, please, everybody . . . but that darned hairdresser . . . and I was frantic."

"I knew everything would be hunky-doodley." Chick crowed after our guests had departed. "Ezra ate his head off . . . and his wife had a wonderful time. She's a honey, isn't she?"

"She's more than a honey."

"Daff was charming too. . . . And Ashley. . . ."

"Uh huh."

"And didn't the kittens make a hit? Weren't they stupendous?"

"Yes. They made me very, very proud."

"You did too, Ernie. Say, let's do this again next Saturday night . . . invite a big crowd to a home-cooked meal."

"First, find me a cook, won't you?"

"Where's your confidence? When will you learn to use all your talents? If I'd wanted a baby as a wife . . ."

"In some ways, you have one, Chick."

"Horse feathers. After tonight, you should be able to tackle any job successfully."

"Thanks for the build-up. I believe in you too."

"You should. Because good men are scarce, remember. And getting scarcer."

CHAPTER 5

Pink Paint and Window Shades

NEITHER Chick nor I have been able to understand exactly why we moved seven times during our seven years on Washington Square. Perhaps we prided ourselves on being rolling stones. Perhaps we enjoyed the excitement of starting fresh again and again. Perhaps this way we prolonged the feeling of being a free-as-birds twosome. In any case, we needed that period of tasting experience and growing up together before we moved to Long Island.

The trek to Linville, a suburb of New York City, was forced by one utterly unbelievable development. For in October 1938, we were expecting a baby in another four weeks.

While the moving men thumped about their business that sparkling fall morning, we stood arm in arm. "Everything we've wanted here at last," Chick sighed.

The fruit of our labors, I thought. And we'll know how to appreciate them.

It was hard to believe that we would be living in this white clapboard house with its fringe of hedge. How, we asked ourselves, could a modest rent bring this luxury of three bedrooms, a fireplace in the living room and a breakfast nook? How had we come to possess this area of grass and green smells, the unhindered view of trees and sky? What had led us to a spot so convenient to the shopping center and railroad station?

In the midst of such ecstasy, present and future problems were forgotten. Yet they were there of course: I would be working as a buyer for another two weeks before starting a short leave of absence. Though we had managed to sign a lease, give instructions on redecorating and hire a moving man, we had been too busy for anything else.

Once we had absorbed the wonders of our new home, Chick and I got busy. Starting with the kitchen, we unpacked cartons, scrubbed shelves, polished windows. Moving in a new rhythm together, we finished chore after chore. And this honeymoon might have continued except for two setbacks.

At noon, when we went into the living room at last, Chick clapped his hands to his eyes. "Hell and Maria, Ernie. These walls are a nightmare. Did you order that screaming pink?"

"It's . . . different, isn't it?"

"Different? Do you expect me to live in this bordello boudoir? Do you?"

"The color I picked was sweet; but the painters went berserk. I wasn't here to check them."

"Why did you want *pink?*"

"A decorator in the store suggested it."

"For Pete's sake, haven't you a mind of your own? Must you be a dumb-Dora clinging vine?"

"I'll tone this down somehow."

"Honestly, honey . . ." Putting both hands on my shoulders, he spoke with deadly seriousness. "I wish you'd taken some art courses in school instead of all that English and economics. . . ."

Ignoring this old bone of contention, I began to brood about curtains as an antidote. Perhaps chintz in beige and brown, with a touch of salmon, would solve everything. Of course I'd never be able to find anything ready-made. No matter. I'd dig up the right fabric somewhere and start a sewing project. Besides, once I was home for a while, it would be good to keep busy.

The other crisis came that night as we started to undress. We had been admiring our first bedroom, its gay flowered walls, maple furniture and hand-hooked rugs. Then as Chick started to haul down the shade, he stared at me hopelessly.

Reviewing his gestures inch by inch, I wondered if he had stepped on some large pointed object.

"Where are they, Ernie?"

"What are you talking about? Must you swoop around like this without any warning?"

"Don't give me that startled-fawn look. Can't you see we haven't any shades here?"

Me oh my, I thought. Living in a goldfish bowl will be inconvenient.

After searching the house, Chick returned fuming. "Every window in this house is bare as a bone."

"Did you search the closets?"

"Certainly. Why didn't we notice this before?"

"Why would we?"

He tried to speak patiently. "You're the woman of this team, honey. Don't decency and privacy seem important, for goodness' sakes?" He draped his bathrobe over the curtain rod. "Well, this is better than a Minsky display, I suppose."

He didn't guess, nor did I, that we would spend the next weeks seeking shades futilely.

The next days tumbled by, leaving unforgettable flashes. There was the morning when our old coal furnace went out. After calling himself a "damn idiot" for moving to the country, Chick made me accompany him to the cellar. "This may happen again, once you're home full time. So watch me carefully."

I yawned.

In two-syllable words he explained about drafts and the rest. "Say it back to me now."

I couldn't.

"You're hopeless, Ern. I wouldn't believe any woman could be so stupid."

"Sometimes it's smart to be stupid," I said, yawning again.

A few days later when Chick was hauling some ashes toward the street, the can fell with a crash on his toes. "Why you blankety no-good so-and-so," he howled, kicking it galley-west.

"Neighbors must know we live here now," I said as he appeared covered with soot.

"The hell with neighbors. If they don't sympathize with me, they damn well should."

There was the Sunday when we got acquainted with the couple next door. Babbie and Si Taylor were newlyweds who had come the day we did. A glimpse of Chick had made them conclude he was a college freshman. Now, after observing my maternity dress, they did a double take. "Goodness, Mr. Carey. You must be older than you look."

Soon we were chatting together like old friends. "We're completely settled," Babbie said. "Curtains hung, pictures up, everything."

"Rooty-toot-toot for us," her husband chorused.

We didn't try to conceal our envy. "How about window shades?"

"They were where they should be in every room."

"Ours weren't," Chick said drily. "Ernie's ordered some. But the shipments keep getting lost."

Now Babbie led us through every corner of her home, including the cellar. There was a new oil furnace there, presenting no problems. Her living room was beige and not reminiscent of a bordello boudoir. Everything was immaculate and shining. Verily she was an excellent housekeeper.

Next we met Aunt Pearl, who had come to visit for a while. "So that young man we saw is your husband. My . . . my . . . precocious, isn't he?" She surveyed my middle like a wise old bird. "Hmmm, that baby's coming soon, isn't he? The way you're carrying he's sure to be a boy."

Then when she heard that I would be working in New York for another week, "You've no business kiting around the streets, dear. Only yesterday I read about a woman delivering on the pavement."

Babbie had fetched some steaming cups of coffee. We sat smiling at each other.

"Now, Mrs. Carey," Aunt Pearl continued, taking another long look at my waistline. "You know best, I hope, choosing a City doctor and hospital. Only once you get those hard pains, call Babbie, understand? We've plenty of clothesline here; she can tie you down safely." Then as Chick scowled, "In labor your wife's apt to kick and fight, young man. Women do sometimes."

My mouth had become very dry. Me, bucking like a billy goat? Needing to be restrained with rope?

Chick gripped my fingers. "She'll sail through this like everything else," he said slowly. "But we're glad you're close by, Babbie. And we'll call you if we need you."

Ah, this man. How had I found him or managed to land him?

A week later on Monday, I climbed into a housedress instead of business clothes. After Chick went off to work alone, I returned to the kitchen for a second cup of coffee. And a third. And a fourth.

While enjoying this luxury, I scribbled the essential things to do today, tomorrow and next week. First things must come first, I thought, setting "window shades" at the top of my list. And last things last, winding up with "frame Chick's baseball picture." If this could wait eight years another few days wouldn't matter.

In the afternoon, I began to interview housekeepers and baby nurses. Or rather, they interviewed me. "How big is this house, ma'am? Six rooms? Well, since they're small maybe . . ." . . . "I always keep my infants in a cool temperature, Mrs. Carey. Doctors agree it helps the respiratory system, so I shall have to insist . . ."

Eventually I arranged for Mrs. Doyle to come six days a week and for Miss Sawyer to take care of the baby. Meanwhile the household chores had slipped into an easy routine with time left for extra jobs: checking on window shades (since the shipment had been lost again), arranging books and sewing, sewing, sewing.

Though some prospective mothers may confess a sudden passion for Limburger cheese or champagne, my curtain assignment became an obsession. Having bought material, rented a machine and equipped myself with needles and thread, I sat on the floor, measuring and stitching interminably.

Only a woman can understand the agony of purchasing, as a last-ditch solution to a color problem, ten identical remnants of figured chintz. Or the ordeal of matching the design inch by inch and flower by flower when the yardage is scant. With a two-week deadline, I had committed myself to the making of five pairs of lined, pinch-pleated draperies. And I was completely unskilled.

Challenged by the problem one minute and ready to kick myself the next, I kept praying that I would finish in time. It would be lovely, I thought, to solve the living-room dilemma before we dashed off to the hospital. Perhaps Chick would hug me wildly. "Ernie, you gem, you genius, you sweet, skillful girl. That pink is perfect now. Why didn't I see its possibilities before?"

But in the midst of this reverie, I'd stab my finger or mismeasure the material. Until Chick's voice seemed to be wonderfully close again. "You gem, you genius, you . . ."

Besides sewing, I made a practice of shopping groceries every day. Clad in a giant polo coat, saddle shoes and socks, I'd debate my choice of bread or pickles. Then laden with packages I'd breeze home again, enjoying the October sunshine and the smell of burning leaves.

Ah, this was really living. Sometimes I wished that days like this, pleasures like this, could continue forever.

Often on these excursions I'd crowd in other errands. Toward the end of the month when our shades again failed to come, I placed my order locally. At the same store, reaching the end of my list at last, I arranged to have a mirror mended and the old photograph framed.

Though Chick and I appreciated only the practical features of shades and mirrors, we were finicky still about our pictures. Close association had made us treasure this special one. Though it was crumpled and going gray by now, I was sure that the Wellesley "top-stringers" would thrive under glass and careful mounting. Chick would be overcome by my thoughtfulness too. "You found time for *this,* you darling, dedicated, little fool?"

Throbbing with pleasure I heard myself speaking aloud now. "Don't go on so, dear. It's nothing really."

"Eh?" the shopkeeper asked, after an incredulous stare. "Who's going where? Not me."

"Sorry, I'm alone a lot lately and I keep talking to myself. . . . Let's see. I'm getting this picture framed as a surprise. Since it means everything to my husband, please take very, very great care."

"You will be pleased. Don't worry." He ducked toward the ringing telephone. "Yes, missus. Your husband left your deceased mother here a while ago. She's to be framed in heavy gold scroll. Right? . . . I know. I know. He told me already. . . ." After he had hung up, he scrawled some notes and glared. "You women and your yackety yack yack."

When he had written my order, "three-eighth inch plain stock," on his pad, he promised again, "You will be pleased."

"Right."

The following morning, I finished, pressed and hung my curtains. The fact that five guests were coming to dinner that night had made this accomplishment seem more vital than ever. Tingling with pride and anticipation, I was in no mood to heed Aunt Pearl's last warning. "That baby's coming any minute. Why try to cook for us, child?"

Yet lately I had been aware of a new sensation thrusting into my chest and throat. But activity was good, the doctor had said. "You'll be more comfortable if you keep moving."

By midafternoon I felt like a runner reaching the final tape. Everything on my list had been completed. The living room was fine at last. The nursery was set. My suitcase was packed. The dining room was ready for tonight's festivities. Now once I had picked up the shades and picture, I could start fussing with dinner.

Bravo, I thought, as I climbed into my coat and started for the store. And a double bravo, I thought again, when I found the shades and mirror looked gorgeous. Now we'll have some privacy . . . and Chick's bathrobe can go back in the closet.

As the shopkeeper reached for my picture, we looked fondly at each other. Anyone can accomplish anything if he tries, I thought. Even if it takes eight years. When the heart and brain reach together toward a goal . . .

A chilling sensation settled suddenly in my stomach. No. Oh no. How could this have happened? How?

The Wellesley sluggers lay on the counter, ensconced in a gold casket, their gray faces and uniforms grayer than ever. Those poor boys taken so young; those poor dear boys.

"Beaudeful. And like I told your husband, only four-fifty, missus."

Everything blurred out of focus and my throat kept twinging. Oh Chick . . . Oh Eddie . . . Oh Dave . . . I'm so sorry . . . so terribly sorry.

"What's the matter, missus? You sick?"

I came alive, sputtering. "You mixed up my order. Right? You put on the wrong frame. Right? And I don't like it a bit. Right?"

"No. Not right. I wrote everything down on the slip but you kept yacketing. Now you've changed your mind."

We argued back and forth a while. "So, missus, take your picture and pay four-fifty. Or I keep it here . . . with your mirror and shades. Understand?"

"But you can't do this. You can't." Suddenly all this seemed too much. Gulping, I plunged out the door toward home.

The plans for our dinner party fell into confusion. How cruel and unfair that man had been. How unethical. And Chick would say so too, wouldn't he, when he heard the story? He'd roll up his sleeves, rush to the store and defend his little wife.

For the next few hours, I dabbled at my work. Somehow I managed to fix hors d'oeuvres and the rest. But I overlooked the fact that we would be eating meat tonight and that it belonged, long since, in the oven.

Finally Chick appeared, discovered the curtains and declared they were perfect. Then I described my afternoon debacle. "That mean man. Thank goodness you're here, honey, to make him see the light."

Instead of welcoming his Sir Galahad role, Chick groaned. "The picture was fine as it was, Ernie. Why didn't you leave it alone?"

"You too, Brutus?" I whispered.

"You baked up this needless fruitcake, Ern. Why wish it on me?"

Why indeed! Oh. Oh. Oh.

"You know I hate stupid rows. When a grown woman starts something like this, she should finish it herself."

"But Chick . . ."

"All right," he said finally. "I'll see what I can do. Only next time . . ."

Why do little things seem to matter and hurt too much lately? I wondered after he had gone. Is it because the walls of our home are confining us too closely now? What's happened to that old ride-with-the-punches team we've been before, darn it? Will we get back into the swing once I return to work?

A few minutes later, Chick returned with the shades, mirror and unframed photograph. But there was no air of triumph. "I was sorry for the poor guy. He did his best to please you, he says, and wrote down your instructions very carefully. And, well . . . you women."

"What? Are you taking his side?"

"Of course." Chick strode over to the mirror and set the photograph in its base. "Why change what we like? Let's keep this here where it belongs."

"You'll always take a man's side? Why, Chick?"

"For the same reason you'll always take another woman's side. Because, damn it, it's right." He clog-stepped toward me and grinned.

We stood together silently until I murmured into his shoulder, "Sometimes I don't understand you, Chick."

"Nor I you. But let's keep trying."

Soon I heard him rattling the icebox. "Say, honey, aren't we having *this* for dinner tonight?" He appeared, bearing an enormous leg of lamb.

"Dear me, yes. How could I be so careless?"

"We can't eat until ten o'clock now."

"I know. I know. Give it to me quick."

As we slammed the roast into the oven, the first guests arrived. Next we were introducing our neighbors, Babbie, Si and Aunt Pearl, to Ashley and Daphne Dodge. "If anyone's hungry for the next few hours, please fill up on hors d'oeuvres."

Eventually I described my difficulty with picture framing. "And you know what? Instead of being sympathetic, Chick scolded me."

"He should," Ashley said, ignoring Daphne's cries of dismay. "A man has troubles enough without settling those of his wife."

We women made clacking noises together. "For shame. How unreasonable."

Exchanging resolute glances, the men ignored us. "Brother," they seemed to tell each other. "But you are so right, brother."

While the fraternity discussed worldly matters, we swapped ideas on childbirth. Though our knowledge was painfully scant, Aunt Pearl kept speaking as an authority. "That baby's due any minute. I've told Ernie she has no business entertaining tonight; but she *would* do it."

Eventually we switched to the subject of layettes. "What?" she demanded, after learning that I had collected a unique yellow ensemble. "Are you possessed to jinx that child? What next?"

At ten-thirty we sat down to dinner. "My," Daphne said, after sampling dessert and coffee, "as a cook you've come a long way, Ern. Everything is divine."

"She's learning," Chick said, his voice deep with pride. "Though sometimes I have to keep pushing her."

"If a woman has capabilities, that's a husband's job," Ashley said. "If she wastes what she's got, no couple can be happy."

"This fandangle talk doesn't make sense to me," Aunt Pearl said. "In my day . . ."

"This is a new day, though," Ashley reminded her smilingly.

"Men still wear the pants . . ."

"Of course. They do and they should. But marriage is a partnership in the very best sense."

"He's on his favorite subject now," Daphne said as Aunt Pearl looked annoyed. "We never should have started this."

As she spoke, I felt my first pain. Oh dear, I thought. How inconvenient. Can't this wait a while, please?

An hour later, when I knew it couldn't and wouldn't,

we called the doctor. "I'm going to get you into New York immediately," Chick said. "Where's that suitcase?"

"Upstairs, honey. But there's no real rush."

Our friends clustered around us, concerned and hushed. Aunt Pearl was wringing her hands. "Can Chick handle you all the way to the City, child? He's strong, of course, but if you start cavorting around . . ."

"I won't."

"You modern girls. No one can tell you anything. But I remember a woman years ago, carried on like the furies . . ."

Chick had put a coat around my shoulders. "You'll excuse us, won't you, folks?" He sounded serene and sure.

I looked up at him, at the warmth and strength there always. There was nothing to worry about. Nothing.

CHAPTER 6

Make Way for Baby

THOUGH Chick had set his heart on a son, he was delighted with his new daughter. "She's cute as a bug," he'd say when he visited the hospital at night.

Bug? This tiny, blond, fragile, blue-eyed creature? Hadn't countless cherubs been bypassed before she had been chosen and braceleted "Baby Carey"? (It seemed silly to admit this conviction, though. Clearly it was a mother's conceit, conflicting with genetic theory.)

"Isn't she beautiful?" I'd ask as we sat holding hands and munching apples.

"She'd better be beautiful . . . if we're going to marry her off at eighteen with the help of God."

In spite of the rigors of institutional care (early morning awakenings, crackling uniforms, thermometers and miserable meal trays) there were happy moments here: the visits of family and friends, of my obstetrician, that precious Godlike man, the baskets of chrysanthemums arriving day after day and the endless gifts.

Aunt Pearl had sent pint-sized blue bootees with an

apologetic note. "Got my signals mixed the way you were carrying. Never went wrong before but love anyway. Hope these will come in handy, dear little mother."

Chick and I enjoyed the telegrams too. Together we read the message from my brother Jack. "Three cheers on coming-out party, Ernie, you minx."

We memorized the teaser from one of my favorite business friends. "Dear Ern. Congratulations. Please tell her early in life that the cash discount is 2% not 5; the sale is outright, not consignment; and there is no advertising allowance. Greetings to you and Papa."

Best of all, Chick appreciated the sentiments of his card-playing cronies. "We have called a super-special meeting to celebrate amid the fragrant odor of Corona-Corona and Joseph Zilch Champagne, Sec 1776. If she's blond, introduce us pronto, Dad."

There were unforgettable letters like the one from my sister Anne, the mother of three school-age boys by now. "Really, Ern, does anything compare with this? . . . Don't you appreciate Mother more than ever before in your life and wonder how she *did* it? . . . Before long you will be admiring your gorgeous new figure and itching to be home and have the baby to yourself. I hope you are settled with a good maid and nurse. . . . Try to build your strength. Love to you, Chick and darling Jill."

Sometimes a cloud blocked off this sunshine. Like the day the chief nurse brought an entourage of doctors on inspection. Enjoying my newspaper, I had flung it page by page over the floor. Basking in the midst of this rubble, I heard an icy good-morning. "Mercy, Mrs. Carey. Are you responsible for this mess? For shame."

But a visiting delegation from my office made everything right, later. They stood in the doorway, those five smiling girls, laden with flowers and packages. "Hello. Hello. Hello."

After we had kissed and opened everything joyfully, they tried to accept their buyer in this new role: as a woman who had borne a child, a person divorced from the store, wearing a lacy nightgown and ribbons in her hair. "Don't you feel different, Miss Gilbreth? . . . I mean, isn't it . . . ?"

"I miss you lots," I told them. "And returning to work will seem good. Yes, it's all very different."

Shortly before leaving the hospital there was the mothers' class attended in bathrobes. Sitting stiffly together, we learned to bathe our babies, to fold diapers the new way and fix formulas. Until one member of the group lost patience. "This old maid speaks nonsense," she shrilled, scowling at the instructor. "You do your kid *so* and you drown him good."

Ignoring such comments, the nurse went on and on, swinging her doll expertly and delivering her patter. "Hold him with his head supported on your wrist. Wash his face first with a soft cloth and no soap."

At last, one beautiful morning, all this lay behind us. Trembling with excitement I got into street clothes sizes too large and flapping ridiculously. Though my figure may have been gorgeous, there was no time to inspect or appreciate it. For Chick was here with suitcases. And Miss Sawyer, the tight-lipped nurse we had employed, was bundling Jill into going-away finery.

Next came the moment when we stood near the cashier cages while the bill was paid. Then at last we were outdoors in the November wind, a part of it and free, free, *free.*

The days and weeks which followed were a bumble of new sensations, sounds and smells.

There was the constant physical weariness mixed with unbelief at our blessings; the urge to cry over nothing. There were the times when we held our daughter while Miss Sawyer hung overhead like an eagle. "Before touching her, did you wash your hands carefully? Isn't Daddy holding his face too close?"

There were the crisp little sermons about keeping Baby "safe, cozy and comfyish." About not sniffing the back of her neck even though it smelled wonderful. There was the odor of talcum, of fresh linen and soap. And the kitchen overflowing with bottles, codliver oil, pablum, strained vegetables and the ritual producing scraped beef. And the bathroom with its jumble of baby scales and jars.

"Baby's ruling the roost," Chick complained as he kept tripping over the bathinette. "Once upon a time *we* lived here too."

"I can't criticize Miss Sawyer for being so persnickety," I said. "Once I'm back at work, we'll know Jill has the best possible care."

"But I'm getting to be a Lady Macbeth, washing my hands until they're raw. Out, out, damn spot."

"Me too, darn it."

When Miss Sawyer took her first day off, Jill became ours at last. Ignoring every rule, we dressed her like a doll, played and sang endlessly. "She's sort of sweet," Chick said, hugging her till she squealed.

Far too soon, the evening brought a key scraping in the lock, the tread of rubber soles, the rustle of skirt marking the end of our pleasure. "Good evening, Mr. and Mrs. Carey. I'm here safely, after such a splendid day. It's brisk outside, isn't it?"

There was the unforgettable time when my brother Frank and several former collegemates came to call. Knowing his skill with young ones, I let him take ours and toss her over his head.

Miss Sawyer, walking noiselessly, arrived at the moment that Baby "shot her cookies." "Good God," Frank screamed, "a towel, somebody, quick."

"Before we touch Baby, Mr. Gilbreth, we always wash our hands."

"And afterwards we take a bath," Frank said, "and burn up our clothes. What a Vesuvius!"

There was the Saturday night shortly before I returned to work. Chick had gone to the kitchen for a midnight snack. Probing in the darkness for a light chain, he sensed someone just a breath away. "Eeoooww, who is it?" he screamed, the hairs hackling at the back of his neck.

"Don't be alarmed, Mr. Carey. Don't be alarmed. It is I, Miss Sawyer, here to fix Baby some water."

"You fixed me instead."

When he returned to our bedroom, he was still pale. "She crept up like a ghost. Those damn rubber soles."

"But they're so safe and cozy, honey. So comfyish."

"They wrecked my liver and lights, I tell you."

Since Miss Sawyer was unusually competent and dedicated, we couldn't complain. Yet we wished she'd had more experience with parents wishing their child close by always. Even at meals.

"What good can come of this, Mrs. Carey? Isn't Mother being selfish?"

"I hope not," I'd say, praying that these times meant as much to Jill as to us.

The other big frustration began to be Miss Sawyer's skill in the stock market. While Chick and I put every cent into rent, food and baby care, she kept buying and selling at a profit. "A former employer phones regularly and gives me tips. Ontario Limited will split two-for-one, in case you're interested."

"At this rate we'll be working for our nurse pretty soon," Chick predicted. "She's raking in cash, isn't she?"

"I wonder what it feels like."

"I wish I knew."

Finally the morning came when I put on smart new business clothes again. Walking toward the railroad station, it seemed right to be at Chick's side. With home responsibilities under control, wasn't I ready to return to my job?

As I'd waved good-by to Jill, there had been a flicker of doubt. Instantly, though, the mother in me and the buyer in me seemed to join hands, repeating a familiar chorus. "Weren't you raised and educated to do exactly this? Would you want it otherwise?"

Once we were on the train, exhilaration came bounding. Ahead lay the chance to learn and to build side by side, each using his talents. Beyond this, beyond the living of each day, a bigger pattern might be developing, of course. But with so many odds and ends to collect, who could think twice about it yet?

My roles as mother and buyer merged a few days later when a delegation from my departments came to visit us. After consuming coffee and cake that evening, they said to Chick, "We sprang a surprise on your wife, her first day at work. She got a bang from it too."

"You knocked me off my feet," I said.

"We knew she'd head into her office first, Mr. Carey. So we strung up diapers there, put a doll on her desk . . . and 'Welcome Home, Mom' signs everywhere. Then when she opened the door, we started singing."

"For a minute I thought she was going to bawl," somebody said. "It was wonderful."

As usual these men and women had brought gifts representing a deep personal sacrifice. "It's nothing," they said, as we swooned over the silver porringer, cup and napkin ring engraved with Jill's name. "Just a little token."

Now Miss Sawyer came sweeping towards us with Baby in her arms. Three cheers, I thought. She's replaced the usual nightgown with a dress even though it's not so cozy and comfyish. Praise the Lord.

While the men hushed, the girls twittered approvingly. "Isn't she adorable? Look at those dear little fingers and toes."

Miss Sawyer unbent with a ghostly sort of smile.

"And look at that darling nose; no bigger than a button."

While everyone was looking, Jill bobbled and burped loudly. The girls flushed as the men grunted, "Bull's-eye, Jillie. Don't blame you a bit."

"We forgot our company manners," our nurse said. "Didn't we, Baby?"

Two years sped by with Miss Sawyer continuing to play the market like a tycoon. Jill was sitting in a high chair, suddenly; then crawling, walking, saying a few words. Golden-haired, all little-girl, she was everything she should be.

The emphasis on Baby's schedule, handwashing and prevention of germs stayed unchanged. Until the blessed day that our nurse gave notice. "I've bought a little apartment building in New York. There's no reason for me to work any more really."

"Of course," we said. "We understand perfectly."

Next came Theresa, an Irish girl, who played with her pet like a puppy, taught her to dance, sing and turn somersaults. During the winter, she and Jill, in identical red bunny-caps, frolicked through the snow together. From May until October, they sunned themselves, gardened and strung beads.

Chick and I were ready to dance, sing and turn somersaults too. And Theresa shared our pleasure. "Faith, why shouldn't you enjoy your dear? 'Twould be a sad thing if you didn't."

Oh, the comfort of such understanding, combined with gaiety and good sense.

Six months later when Theresa married we said hello and good-by to nurses in sequence. There was Fritzie, who proved to be pregnant; and Myra of the mascara and long blond curls; and Sandra, who snored and left the door invitingly open; and Niobe with bosoms like watermelons, who pawned our silver.

Finally, when we had reached the end of endurance, when we had agreed, "One more new face here and we'll return to the city," we employed Mrs. Twinum as housekeeper and mother's helper.

Though Twiney came with only one suitcase, her worldly possessions kept spawning. Eventually we were able to identify three trunks, clothes filling two closets, lamps, a bookcase, a complete bedroom suite, a chaise longue, pictures and an umbrella rack.

"Good God," Chick said, after taking inventory. "That woman should be paying us warehouse rental. When did she sneak this stuff in . . . and why do you allow it?"

"After she lost her husband, she lost her home. Her possessions are all she has left in the world now. And since she's such a dear with Jill . . ."

"Must we keep that dratted umbrella rack underfoot?" he asked, stumbling into it again and again.

"It's impossible to find domestic help in the country."

"This time you found the impossible. We're being crowded back into the wall."

"But I hate to hurt her feelings."

"How about mine?" He kept rubbing his leg.

While we were in the midst of this argument, Twiney's little grandson came to visit. "It's only for a day or two,"

I told Chick. "Another child will be good company for Jill."

But Peter was anything but good company. "He'll calm down in time," Twiney promised as he chipped paint and mutilated wallpaper, "and since his mother's taken that nervous breakdown . . ."

Soon Jill was following him like a slave. "You stink, Mom," she told me one night. "You stink out loud."

"Lovely," Chick said, glaring at me. "If you don't get rid of these poachers, I'll give them the heave-ho."

Inevitably, after a scene like this, Twiney would show us photographs of her husband, of the old Passaic apartment and the family burial plot. "That dear man meant to provide for me . . . but, well, he didn't."

During the final months in Linville, we ate better than ever before or since: home-baked pastry, vegetables cooked to perfection, the choicest cuts of meat. Whenever I ordered hamburger or liver, we sat down to steak instead. "Lester owns the market, Mrs. Carey . . . and he loves to do favors."

"Bring him around sometime," Chick urged. "How about tomorrow night?"

"For shame, you old matchmaker," I said later.

"Listen. I'd stop at nothing to get her out of here. With her furniture and blasted grandson too."

After her first date with Lester, Twiney began to wear gay print dresses, a halo of lavender curls and carnation perfume. "He's so dear and lovely," she'd say, "and if you'll let us use the living room again tonight . . ."

When they were married a month later, Chick couldn't conceal his joy. "Praise God and good riddance," he said, helping to hoist the umbrella rack into the van.

"We almost had it for keeps," I said.

"Hell's bells. Don't I know it."

"Sometimes you have flashes of real brilliance, Chick. But this is going to cost you some new furniture when we move to New York. That apartment we've taken is awfully big."

"Praise God," he said again.

CHAPTER 7

New York Was Never Like This

Of our nine homes in eleven years, this sprawling apartment on East Nincticth Street was the handsomest. "Do we really live here?" Chick and I would ask each other sometimes. "It's too lush almost."

Too lush or not, this had been the only place offering enough space for us, a nurse and a sleep-out cook. "Jill can run her legs off here," I said as Chick signed the lease.

"Run . . . hell. She can set up a bowling and billiard establishment."

In this aura of beige and biscuit tones, of rich draperies and entire walls of bookcases, we could relax as a family. During business hours Jenny and Tender Job would keep an eye on Jill.

But in spite of their affection, in spite of nursery school, visits to the park and dancing lessons, she seemed to be lonely. Though she had a room of her own bursting with toys, she kept hugging us till it hurt. "Oh Mommy. Oh Daddy, Daddy."

"Ouch, honey. Do you want to break my neck?"

"Take me with you. Everywhere," she'd plead again and again.

"We wish we could," we'd say. "But come along now anyway. Let's go to the drugstore and get some chocolate ice cream for supper."

Then as we walked out into the night air together, she'd be in an ecstasy. "Oh Mommy, oh Daddy, this is good."

"I know," we'd say, resolving to give her a more normal life as soon as we could.

One evening we found her in the living room performing for her family of dolls. There was Betsy resplendent in pink satin, Rubbery, an ancient baby minus an arm and smelling like a crib pad, Raggedy Ann and the rest. Close by the phonograph jerked out Beethoven's Minuet in G while Jill did ballet steps learned that afternoon. "Watch me now, children. Step and step and step and step; point your toe."

Several weeks before, she had started dancing classes at our pediatrician's suggestion. This was in the hope of developing better muscular coordination rather than any Hollywood aptitudes. Still, as we introduced ourselves to Mme. Petrof, I couldn't help feeling like a tiny screen star's mother.

The studio, in the theater district, carried the essence of an unventilated basketball game mixed with chalk and musk. ("This stinks," Jill said, wrinkling her nose. "This really stinks.")

Madame, a former ballerina, wore purple slacks accentuating her enormous behind. While her stoooodents leaped in unison, she whacked out the beats with a sawed-off billiard cue. Step and step. Point your toe.

She would halt the rendition of Beethoven and administer discipline frequently. "You, Sonyaaa, wake up and waaatch me." (Crash went the cue against the floor.) "Otherwise you go home and staaay, lazy one."

I had been afraid that Jill would wince at Madame's hawklike personality. Instead she took all two hundred pounds of her to her bosom. And made a sort of goddess image of her too. "I'm going to eat all my pudding and get lovely and strong," she'd say worshipfully. "Madame says I should. . . . I'm going to practice my steps to-night, because Madame says . . . You know, Mommy, I just love Madame. Don't you?"

"What the devil has this Madame got?" Chick asked, tantalized with curiosity. "Why this sudden crush?"

"I wish I knew myself, honey. I can't explain it. Except . . . you've heard about friendships developing, say, between horses and pigeons, haven't you? . . . Or dogs and kittens?"

"Yes. Of course. So what?"

"So . . . well, something similar has happened here. I can't explain it. But praise God, anyway."

Next to dancing, reading had become Jill's favorite pastime. Just before bedtime we always rehashed "The Princess and the Pea." "Please, Mommy," she'd say, her cheek warm against mine, "the best one now."

While Chick buried himself in the newspapers, I'd tell about the shrewd old queen testing the princess as a fit wife for her son. "She took twenty mattresses and twenty featherbeds and piled them on the pea, because on top of all this, the princess would be sleeping that night."

"Then what?"

". . . The princess went to bed cozy and comfyish." (This detail never failed to rouse Chick from the sporting page with a snort.)

"And then what?"

"In the morning the queen asked the princess, 'Did you sleep well?' . . . 'No indeed,' she cried, 'my whole body is black and blue.' Then, of course, the queen knew that this was a real princess, because nobody else could have such a delicate skin."

Jill's other favorite story was the one about the magic cereal dish. Excitement grew boundless as we reached the mother on the chimney, shrieking, "Help, help."

"Tell me how she looked, Mommy."

"This time you tell me."

"Cereal was in her nose. And in her toes. And in her shoes. And in her socks."

Soon Jill began to test these tales. Early one morning,

she yipped into our bedroom. "Am I black and blue, Daddy? Last night I put a button under my mattress."

"Of course you're not black and blue," Chick said, after examining her.

Bursting into tears, she ran back to her room.

"What's eating that child, Ern?"

"Well . . . now she knows she isn't a princess."

"Whatever made her think she might be?"

Rushing to comfort her, I paused long enough to explain.

"Stop filling that child with nonsense. Or some day you'll regret it."

The regret came all too soon. We had been reading the rhyme about the old woman on the King's Highway.

> There came a peddler whose name was Stout
> He cut her petticoats all round about
> He cut her petticoats up to the knees
> Which made the old woman shiver and freeze.

If Jill looked thoughtful during her bath, I didn't notice it that Sunday night. Crouched on my knees afterwards, scrubbing the tub, I didn't expect trouble. Perhaps I was too busy trying to protect my dress from splashing soap powder.

As I gave the porcelain a final swipe, something cold touched my legs. Click. Click. Click. Overhead Jill stood fingering a pair of scissors.

Rising in slow motion, I examined the back of my skirt

and its broad slash. "Lawk a mercy on me, this be none of I."

Jill guffawed. "My, you look funny."

I stood dumfounded.

"Your dress looks funny too . . . and your garters."

Taking the scissors silently, I went into her bedroom. What should I do next? What would the experts advise, dear God? Pondering and getting nowhere, I saw Betsy the doll in pink satin, sprawled invitingly. Click. Click. Click.

Jill began to screech. "Why did you cut her dress? Why?"

"Great big joke, isn't it?"

"Hell and Maria, girls, what's going on here?" Chick's head popped through the doorway and disappeared. "I didn't dare stick around another minute," he explained later. "You looked like a couple of Eleonora Duses. Ho. Ho."

The next night when we were doing nursery rhymes, Jill suggested that we skip one in particular. "Betsy doesn't like it any more. I don't either."

On week ends we always went to the Park together and fed the squirrels. While Jill zipped down the playground slides, we'd hear the confidences of other parents. "My Jerry is a handful. . . . My Susy is shy, so I encourage her always (with the glance never turned from the little one). . . . Look out, darling. . . . Watch it,

Champ. . . . Easy, Pal. . . . Now it's your turn, lamb."

Amid the love, the layers of too much protection, lay the necessity for each Jerry and Susy to be as expensively dressed as Champ or Lamb. Consequently Mother and Father insisted on custom-made coats, handsewn tailoring, genuine velvet or fur, perky, wildly expensive hats. And English toys, resplendent with chromium.

In contrast we always preferred the Zoo and the people we found there. "My kids sure go nutty here," someone would say to Chick, indicating his flock in dungarees.

"Ours too."

"Yeh. You bet."

These excursions always raised inevitable questions too. New York City was fine for us. But how about Jill?

Occasionally, when I was able to get a free Saturday, we went on movie sprees together. But *Dumbo* was anything but a success. As the theater darkened and the screen swam with elephants Jill began to howl, "Take me home."

"Look, honey. A man made a funny drawing . . ." But I knew we were over our heads.

"It was too terribly awful," she said, as Chick led us outside.

Months later, we made a happier trip to the same spot. This time we danced and pranced with Snow White and the Seven Dwarfs. This time we shared real ecstasy and laughter. Afterwards, Jill kept singing, "Some day my prince will come." She fixed a regal band in her hair and wore her collars turned up to her ears.

"I'm glad we didn't take her to *Dracula,*" Chick said, chuckling. "Can you imagine what we'd be going through?"

"Perish the thought."

"Jill needs more kids to play with . . . and a yard for ball games."

"She keeps begging for a baby sister."

"In time maybe she'll get one. Or a brother."

"Let's not wait too long, honey. Two children are easier to raise than one."

"Not in the city, Ernie."

"Let's move out of the city as soon as we can."

"Is that a promise?"

"Yes."

Though Tender Job, our housekeeper, became a well-loved member of the family, nurses kept going and coming. After Jennie's elopement, we attended Flossie's, Sadie's and Sue's weddings in turn. "All my suits have rice in their pockets," Chick complained. "What are you running here, a marriage mart?"

With their romances severely complicated by the war, our brides found no comfort in Tender Job. "Beware temptation," she'd tell them, pointing to a religious tract. "Marriage brings evil and babies into the world."

"It gets me daffy," the girls would say to me.

Daffy or not, each of them landed her man successfully. But Sue's tearful good-by was the one we remembered best. Drawing the elaborate veil from her face, she kissed Jill repeatedly. "Don't forget me. Please, honey, don't forget me."

"Don't go, Sue. Don't go."

"Why, you're crying, Jillie. And you mustn't."

Stanley, in his seaman's uniform, grew red in the face. "Are you *trying* to make the kid bawl?" he roared to Chick's delight. "Lay off, for goodness' sakes."

"But I'll miss her so."

"On our honeymoon? Ho. Ho. Ho."

Dottie, newly graduated from nursing school, came next. Though she took pride in her stiffly starched uniform, she hated stockings and shoes. "I'm from the country, you know, and I've never liked being bound up. So when I'm inside here . . ."

To Tender Job, going barefoot was poor-white-trash. "I never saw a girl so lax," she'd say loudly.

Dottie was equally outspoken about religious tracts. "That sex stuff leaves me cold," she'd say. "Who's ready for sex yet?"

Praises be, Chick and I would think.

Though we enjoyed casualness in ourselves always, we didn't love it in Dottie. During the evenings she romped through the apartment in her pajamas. When she wasn't on the phone talking with girl friends, she'd chew gum and read comic books. "She's a benighted teen-ager still," Chick would say.

"Granted. But she's an excellent nurse."

"Can't you make her wear shoes or a bathrobe, for Pete's sake?"

"So far, no."

We lived through several months of this while Dottie's phonograph kept blaring "Yankee Doodle" and "Turkey in the Straw." Then after receiving a letter from her family, she packed her bags. "I'm homesick for Little Falls. Pa has a new colt and a neighbor needs a hand with her kids. So long, folks."

Once she had left, Tender Job agreed to devote herself to Jill. "So many new faces aren't good for that child. Or for me either."

In May, Chick brought home the news that his company was folding and he must change jobs. Less than twenty-four hours later, we learned that we would be having a baby in December. Wow, we thought. This will be anything but a picnic. Ouch.

While Chick explored work opportunities, this new young one, like Mary's little lamb, began to make mischief. When the nausea period passed, my figure exploded overnight. Amazed at my increasing girth, I wondered what Aunt Pearl would say. "This time, dear girl, it must be twin elephants."

Eventually Chick joined a Brooklyn manufacturer of precision instruments. Then in late November, my leave of absence began. With the hard days behind us, we could tell each other gaily, "Everyone has his ups and downs. So what?"

During Thanksgiving in Montclair, we were able to celebrate as never before. But the Gilbreths, unfortunately, seemed to be members of the Aunt Pearl Club. "Are you sure you should be here, Ernie? Shouldn't you be in New York, near the hospital?"

"Who's having this baby? You or me?"

No one bothered to answer.

"If it didn't come in the store yesterday, it won't come here."

"Ernie knows best," Mother said quietly. "If she's serene in her mind, we ought to be too."

Though our child wasn't due for another month, he came a week later. Confounding us completely.

Having tucked Jill into bed, I was saying good night to Tender Job. Chick was working late that night and couldn't be reached. A labor pain came; then another.

"You lay down on the sofa," Tender Job said, removing her hat and coat. Big and capable, she sat beside me, smoothing my forehead and checking the clock. Finally she called the doctor.

My mind kept churning. Oh dear, if only Chick were here. Tender Job always spends the night with her "Sisters," doesn't she? We've made no arrangements yet for sleep-in help. If I go to the hospital now, who will care for Jill? My suitcase isn't packed. No layette is ready. This must be a false alarm.

"There, there," Tender Job said, as I started to sniffle. "Put your faith in Father now. I've asked Him to help us and He will."

As the doorbell rang, my heart soared wildly. Maybe this was Chick. But he used his key always. Didn't he?

Lips brushed my cheek. My mother was bending over me and smiling. "Hello, dear. I thought I'd run in and surprise you."

Now everything was all right. Always before in my life and when Jill was born too, she had come. Always she seemed to sense need in her children and to appear immediately.

"Mother, are you really here?"

While I lay dozing, she went off with Tender Job. Soon they were back with my suitcase. "I put in your books, Ernie. And some writing paper. And your favorite cologne."

"Oh Mother, sometimes I love you."

"And what do you suppose? Tender Job will live here

while you're in the hospital. So now you haven't a worry in the world."

"You're kind, Tender Job."

"I know my Father sent your mother to us tonight. This way I can tell Him" — she bowed her head — "thank you, Father."

A latch clicked. "Hi, honey. Where are you? In the living room?"

Mother hurried to meet Chick. They kissed fondly.

"Oh no," he sighed, when he saw me on the sofa. "Must you, Ernie? Tonight?"

"I'm afraid she must, Chick. And isn't it fine?" Mother steered him back toward the door. "Now, dear, if you'll get a taxi, please." As he bounded off, she and Tender Job helped me into my coat.

This time our baby came slowly. But he came at last, the morning of December 5. "He's lovely, isn't he?" I gloated, while Chick's chest expanded. "Imagine having a boy! Could anything be better?"

"Sure. Twins. And I would have bet my last dollar."

"Me too," I said.

CHAPTER 8

Beware the Boy

DURING my stay in the hospital, Chick was Grand Master of the Ancient Order of Proud Papas. He flashed cigars. He smothered the nurses and me with candy. He spent hours outside the nursery observing his future All-American tackle. He opened a banking account dedicated to higher education.

All this was in contrast to his calmness after the birth of a daughter. "And why not?" he asked. "All my life, I've wanted a son and namesake."

"If we can send only one of the kids to college," I teased, "maybe it should be Jill."

"Stuff and nonsense. Who needs a B.A. degree bending over a stove all day?" (The New England roots were a part of him still, clearly. Lackaday.)

As his enthusiasm for his son grew, I worried about its effect on Jill.

"Hell and Maria. Imagine a four-year-old needing special attention. How silly can you be?"

"But the books say . . ."

"Nuts."

At last I was able to leave the hospital. Chick appeared with the usual paraphernalia. Dottie arrived half an hour later. "My bus was late, but I met the cutest soldier. He's asked me to the picture show tonight. . . . Now where's Little Brother? I could eat *brand*-new babies."

"How's Little Falls?" we asked.

"Too dull all of a sudden. I'm glad to be back."

Now the pediatrician came with last-minute instructions. "This fellow's going to be a real buster." After removing Charlie's diaper, he flipped him on his stomach. "Pay no attention to this tiny skin tab at the base of his spine. It's common in premature youngsters and will disappear soon."

My, my, we thought, examining our son. Who says we're more than a jump from monkeys?

Repeating a familiar pattern, we paid the bill and crowded into a taxi. Emerging from the park, we stepped into our building, into the elevator, into our home. Next we hugged Jill and Tender Job while Dottie kicked off her shoes. "Murder. These pinchers are killing me."

"Here we go again," Chick groaned into my ear. "What about that soldier tonight? Are you going to let her see him?"

"We'll see," I said, wondering why decisions like this must be faced so soon.

Carrying the children into our bedroom we counted them again and again. One and one is two. *Two.*

While I undressed and went to bed, Jill held Charlie in a strangle hold. "Why didn't you bring me a sister? Who wants a boy?" Then before I could explain, she began to rock him. "You're my honey. Just like Rubbery. Only you smell gooder."

"You see, Ernie?" Chick whispered. "Didn't I say it would be this way?"

Later, lying there in the sunshine, everything seemed too good to be true. The field flowers on our wallpaper had never looked more fresh; nor the curtains more frothy. Home sweet home.

Ecstasy increased as Tender Job brought in a cup of tea and some cinnamon toast. This heaven can't last, I thought. But it's super.

As she removed the tray, she placed a religious tract on my knees. "Please read this, Mrs. Carey." She bent over me, gray-haired and worried. "Maybe you noticed I *couldn't* look at that baby. According to Father's teachings here . . ."

In the thrill of homecoming, I had been concentrating on Jill entirely. Now this development hit hard and painfully. "But Tender Job, every child is born innocent and helpless . . ."

"Excuse me; but every child is a *sin.* . . . Why do you suppose we Sisters, even we who have been married, live together? Why do the Brothers keep to themselves always? Because this way, we don't fall into temptation. It's all explained here." She pointed to the tract again.

Crash, bang, boom, I thought.

"But I love Jillie, Mrs. Carey . . . and being here too. So if you'll keep that baby out of sight . . ."

Leaning back into the pillows, I sighed.

She hovered overhead still, clearing her throat. "Er . . . there's another thing crowding my conscience. . . . It was lonely evenings, with you and Mr. Carey out. . . . Maybe it was wrong and maybe you'll be cross . . ."

Now what? I wondered.

"I should have asked his permission before taking Jill to our Supreme Banquet. But, well . . . I didn't."

"I bet she had the time of her life."

"Indeed she did. Indeed she did. In her party dress with her shoes all shined."

I drank in the picture.

"After she'd sung on the stage with the other Virgins, she marched straight to Father. 'Hello, I'm Jill,' she said, real proud. My, how everyone laughed and clapped. So Father raised her up beside Him and gave her a turkey drumstick. 'Thank you kindly,' she said. Later, after He'd blessed her, we came home."

"Jill can remember this forever," I said, envying her a little.

"Indeed so. Someday she can tell her children, "I was blessed by Him personally."

"Thank you for telling me, Tender Job."

"Thank you, Father," she said, bowing her head.

I lay thinking about the paradoxes that come sometimes. Jill had accepted her brother lovingly already. But our housekeeper couldn't and probably wouldn't. Unless Charlie inched his way into her heart bit by bit.

Once Dottie had dated with her soldier, she changed overnight. Though she kept to the barefoot routine, she added curlers now and lurid lipstick and nail polish. Whenever the phone rang, she'd palpitate: "I'll answer it, folks. It's Harold calling."

Since this had its comic side, we couldn't help enjoying it. But Tender Job was horrified. "Dottie's too young to be dancing off night after night. She'll come to no good."

"What in the world could happen?" I asked.

"She could fall into temptation . . . like you did."

At last I was able to join Chick at the dinner table again. With Jill beside us, we sat enjoying broiled chicken and back-to-normal family closeness.

"Isn't someone missing here?" Chick asked, glancing bleakly toward Charlie's bedroom.

"He's going to be missing for a while," I said, not liking the situation but resolved to endure it. "Good housekeepers are hard to find. And until I feel stronger . . ."

"Unbalanced characters are easy to find," he said, "or you have a genius for hiring them. I'm not sure which."

"Bull's-eye on both scores," I said.

Occasionally Chick carried me back to bed before dessert. "You're overdoing as usual. Why did you get up so soon?"

Yet we knew that I needed to be "up and overdoing." For the easy time was drawing to an end. In another two weeks, I would be back again at the store; and each day now was all too short.

During this period, Jill and I could scarcely wait for Dottie's first afternoon off. For then, for the first time, we'd care for Charlie ourselves.

Lying in bed, I kept anticipating the pleasures ahead. What is more warming than *being* with your baby, changing him, feeding him, getting really acquainted with his ways and wants? Ah me, I thought.

The big day began with Dottie spending the morning in the bathroom. "I can't even get in there to clean," Tender Job complained. "She's shampooing her hair and putting on a terrible fuss. That girl's a Jezebel."

At noontime Harold came in long enough to meet us all. Blue-eyed, chunky and immaculate in his uniform, he could have been Dottie's brother. "Let's get shuffling, sweet," he told her. "Who wants to hang around here?"

"Are you going to marry Dottie?" Jill asked him.

"Do you think I should?"

"She says she wishes you'd ask her."

"Well maybe I will."

"Hush, Jill," Dottie said, blushing. "I'll never tell you a secret again ever."

When they had left, we got Charlie ready for his feeding. While I folded a fresh diaper, Jill went off to warm the bottle. Meantime I had turned our boy over on his stomach, removed his wet linen and administered some talcum.

Tender Job came through the doorway now, with her eyes averted. "Jill needed some help, Mrs. Carey. I hope the temperature is right." She flicked some drops of milk on my wrist. Then, drawn toward the bassinet, she took a peek.

Whoopee, I thought. We're getting somewhere, aren't we?

"Look at my baby, Job," Jill said, wriggling between us. "See his teeny-tiny toes?"

"Indeed he is cute, Jillie. Indeed he is," Tender Job bent over him smiling.

"See his teeny-tiny tail too? But now it's almost gone."

"He was premature, you know," I said, adjusting a pin.

Tender Job stood crouched and frozen. She backed

slowly toward the hallway. "Forgive them, Father. Forgive them their *sins*."

This is like a hammy scene in the theater, I thought. Is this my voice taking the next cue now? "Don't be afraid, Tender Job. This is nothing unusual really. You're too kind and wise to believe . . ."

After running into the kitchen, she returned with her hat and coat. "I can't stay in this house. It's been marked. That child's been marked. . . . You can mail my salary. . . . Good-by, Mrs. Carey . . . and Jill. Good-by."

As the door slammed, Jill rubbed her eyes. "Doesn't she like Charlie?"

"He suits us, doesn't he?"

"Yes. But why did Job run away so fast? Why?"

"Good riddance," Chick said when he heard the story. "Now let's bring that boy into the dining room. It's time he took his place in this family."

Later, Dottie clattered into our bedroom to share her happy news. "Guess what? He really did ask me. And we're going to be married in the spring."

"He's the speedy type, isn't he?" Chick asked paternally.

"Everyone's speedy in wartime, Mr. Carey. Good men are scarce."

"I've heard that before. It happens that you're right. And I'll buy a bale of rice tomorrow."

"Good." She kicked off her shoes. "These pinchers are killing me. You don't mind, do you?"

"We do; very much," Chick said. "But we know when we're licked. Now get to bed, you blasted teen-ager. And happy dreams."

CHAPTER 9

Land of the Free

How can you identify a resident of Long Island? If he insists what should be north is west, what should be south is east, Bingo! you've got your man. Except for this confusion on local geography, he's like other suburbanites, happy in his home, his family, his American citizenship and his accomplishments.

Perhaps the events immediately preceding our move to Manhasset made us appreciate what we found there. Anyhow, in the spring of 1944 they forced us into a decision which changed our lives.

Looking back on those last months in New York City, I marvel at their impact. Minor little happenings roused us as they did, praise God?

For example, there was the fracas in Central Park where an attendant bawled out Jill. She had picked a spray of forsythia, mutilating public property. Afterwards she was heartbroken. "It looked pretty; I didn't mean to be bad." ("The children belong in the country," Chick fumed. "We're not being fair to them, Ernie.")

Tender Job had been replaced by Glenda, old and

rheumatic. "I meant to clean, Mrs. Carey . . . but my back's bothering me again. . . . I meant to watch that roast but . . ." ("I know our household isn't running right," I'd confess, as we dabbed at our food. "But housekeepers are impossible to find. What can we do?")

Chick's factory moved from Brooklyn to Lake Success, L.I., causing him a long commute. He left at dawn and returned dog-tired. ("I miss visiting with you and the children. Let's look around Great Neck and Manhasset; the homes are beautiful.")

Though we were swinging expenses between us, we couldn't seem to save a nickel. ("If we were having fun out of *this*, money wouldn't matter. But we're breaking our backs for what?")

Dottie, who had spent most of her married life with us, announced that Harold was back from overseas. "He'll be out of the hospital soon and we're going back to Little Falls." ("Of course," we agreed. "Once he's well and on his feet again, you belong there.")

That same day, when I was given a third department to buy for, I began to doubt my strength.

Chick doubted it too. "The good fight's gotten too big for us, Ernie. Let's move to the country. I want you to retire from business. Look at the facts."

"All right," I said, after he had enumerated them. "But confinement at home isn't going to be easy. Once Charlie's ready for school . . ."

"When that time comes we'll see," he promised.

On Sundays after this, we kept combing Long Island. Eventually we decided on the North Shore and Manhasset. Then we found a little gray house on a street swarming with children. Eureka!

We examined its three bedrooms, two baths and oil furnace, its screened porch and simplicity. We marveled at its blooming wisteria, its beech and dogwood trees and velvet lawn. Could anything be more *made for us* ever?

In a hush carrying the sanctity of marriage itself, we signed the first papers. "Pinch me," I said as we were returning to New York. "Pinch me hard."

We got through the next weeks somehow. We listed our apartment with agencies, sought a new job for our housekeeper, made arrangements for moving June first. We learned to be thankful for five hours' sleep and energy which renewed itself somehow.

"We need more hands and another back," I'd wail sometimes.

We placed our housekeeper and sublet our apartment after a frantic delay. We ordered our icebox and porch furniture out of storage, arranged for a woman to clean our new home, gave instructions for utilities to be connected.

Then came June first, D day.

The moving men arrived, swarming like elephants.

Our apartment lay bare, resounding with echoes. We put on our hats and coats, bid Dottie and Glenda good-by, stepped into an elevator, a taxi. We took a last look at our building and street.

Once we were on the train, all this had washed away. Already we seemed to be a new, typically suburban family with Charlie in his sky-blue snowsuit, Jill in a broad-brimmed hat. Mother, dad, son and daughter, I thought, aware of a new closeness, a new simplicity. The backbone of America.

In no time the conductor was bawling from the platform, "Manhasset. Manhasset. Watch yer steps, folks."

We piled into a creaking old limousine while Chick teased, "This cab reminds me of our house, only it's fifty years newer. Don't expect much, kids, today. There's a grocery store on the first floor and gas pumps out in the yard."

"And a backhouse too, Dad?"

"Sure . . . all the very *latest* . . ."

We wound our way up a hill, past the homes, the children on bicycles, into Munsey Park. We swung into our street, marveling at the masses of Paul's scarlets blooming everywhere. We ground to a stop under a bower of greenness and sky.

"Everyone out," Chick shouted. "We're here."

"You were joking before, weren't you, Dad?" Jill asked, as she tumbled out. Then she ran screaming toward the front door. "Look, we've got roses and flowers here. Millions of them."

"We gots . . ." Charlie repeated, trundling after her.

Chick led us into the living room. We rushed from room to room, trying to realize they were ours. "Pinch me," I said to Chick, "the way you did before."

"We're ready for this, Ern. And we'll appreciate it."

"In some ways, it's like starting at the beginning," I whispered.

"With anything and everything possible . . . as always." He caught himself. "Listen to us, yammering like a doggone bride and groom. Remember, we have work to do, for Pete's sake."

"There are no pink walls this time, honey. I picked this blue color myself. And there are shades in every room."

"Praises be."

During the next hours, there was plenty to keep us busy, since the cleaning woman had failed to come. "I wish I could have swept up before the moving men came," I groaned. "And why the phone wasn't connected, I'll never know."

"We're used to dust, thanks to Glenda. And who needs a phone? A little silence will seem good for a change."

But there was no silence, of course, the rest of that day. Or peace of mind either. Though we had moved many times before and cared for the children over week ends, we had never tried to handle both jobs together. "No, Charlie. Stop, Charlie. Please, Charlie," we seemed to say with each breath.

Meantime, bursting with new freedom, he twisted gas levers, crashed end tables and fussed with locks. "Me fix. Me bang. Me . . ."

"Me spank," Chick said, swatting his backsides. "Calm down, you wild Indian, or I'll chain you somewhere."

Jill led three new playmates in and out, round and round, back and forth. One minute they were sliding down the banisters, the next jumping rope or pulling each other's hair. "Can't you squelch that sorority session, Ern? Hell and Maria."

After we had stored away most of the food and kitchen equipment, we paused for a cup of coffee. "Haven't you got sensible shoes somewhere?" Chick asked. "You must be dead on those high spikes."

"I am dead. But not just from shoes. Holy smoke, is it going to be this strenuous?"

"Ho. Didn't you grow up in a big family? In comparison this should be simple."

"With your own kids it's different, Chick. I'm a freshman . . ."

"You aren't either . . ."

"There's so much to learn; patience especially." Swooping, I caught Charlie playing with the meat knife. "See what I mean?"

"No, son," Chick said sternly. "Did you hear me? Daddy says No. Stop or I'll beat your bottom raw."

Giggling, Charlie dived into his lap. "See, Ern? That boy understands already. Talk to him like a man and he'll respond. See?"

Charlie reached up and hugged him. But a minute later he was twirling the knife again.

"I see," I said, as Chick repeated, "Daddy says No."

That night, for the first time since the Linville era, logs crackled in our fireplace. "Heaven knows we don't need them in June," Chick said. "But it's brisk tonight and well . . . why not?"

This is like a Christmas scene, I thought. Only better. There's Chick in his tennis outfit again . . . and thank goodness we're here.

Outside, two cats howled plaintively. Chick listened to them, enchanted. "They remind me of old Nip and Tuck. By golly, we're *home!*"

CHAPTER 10

Adhesive Tape and Small Talk

EIGHTEEN months later we had become real Manhassetites, timing lunch by the fire whistle, supper by the arrival of the evening paper.

Jill and Charlie had dozens of playmates, close as brothers and sisters. They could roll in the yard whenever they pleased. Or yell from the back door, "Hey, if you're making cookies, save the bowl for me."

I had learned to stay in the background while they worked out their difficulties. Like the time Jill was sent home by the neighborhood kids. "I wouldn't follow their rules, so they threw me out of the game. Make them let me play."

I tried to make her see that she must handle this hot potato herself.

"But Dottie always took my side in the city. Why won't you?"

Dragging one foot in front of the other, she finally rejoined her friends. "When mothers try to settle our fights, no one ever likes them," she said a few days later. "If you did that, you'd be a smelly old crow."

One afternoon, Charlie skinned his knee badly. White with fright, he came roaring into the kitchen. "Owww, it hurts."

His screams continued as we went into the bathroom for gauze and antiseptic. "Don't. Don't. Don't."

"Your bruise is nothing, son," I said, "compared to this scratch on the toilet seat. Let's clean and put a bandage on it first."

Once he tried his hand at bandaging the seat, he took pleasure in bandaging himself.

You could teach a seminar in child psychology now, I told myself proudly. Conquer fear and you vanquish all.

Having learned first-aid-to-toilet-seats, Charlie kept plastering them busily. "Me fix, Mom. Me fix."

Fix was right. And a pretty fix indeed as we found ourselves glued embarrassingly, again and again. "Help. Get me off," Jill kept wailing. "I'm stuck and can't wiggle."

"What idiot started this nonsense?" Chick would ask me.

During this period, Jill and I spent hours making doll clothes or shampooing our hair. Often we told continued stories too. She'd pant with suspense as her turn finished and mine began: "Then, Mommy, the witch pushed the princess down the cliff."

After debating the possibilities, I liked to tease her. "But the princess had spikes on her shoes; so she clapped them down crash, bang."

"She didn't either. You're spoiling it. No fair."

And all the time I'd be thinking, What could be finer than this minute right now?

The evenings, when Chick came home from work, were just as they should be too. As we rushed to hug him, he'd shout, "One at a time, folks. One at a time." Wending our way back into the kitchen, Jill would begin a favorite riddle: "Why does Uncle Sam wear red-white-and-blue suspenders?"

Puffing on his pipe, Chick would concentrate on the answer. Meantime Charlie slammed his tractor underfoot.

"You're too slow, everybody. Here's why: to hold up his pants."

"Ho. Ho."

"Here's another. This time I won't help you. What flower do you wear all year round?"

Even Charlie knew this one. "Two lips."

"Here's another. How do you get down off an elephant?"

We couldn't guess.

"You don't get down off an elephant; you get down off a duck."

"Ho. Ho. Ho."

The kitchen would teem with pipe smoke and the savor of stew. When we were ready to serve, Jill would pour the milk while the boys buttered the rolls together. Soon we settled ourselves at the table. One of us would say grace. "Thank you, oh Lord, for these and all thy blessings."

When the dishes had been done, we'd sprawl in the living room, playing Slap Jack or Who Am I? Between games, Jill would describe some excitement at school or her part in a forthcoming play. "I'm going to be the rear end of a horse; so don't expect to see my face tomorrow."

Whenever she drew too much attention, Charlie would lean against his father and stroke his chin. "You nice old daddy."

Sometimes, at the children's insistence, Chick would tell about his New England boyhood. While they hooted with joy, he'd describe "Chickadee" Carey as a protesting five-year-old in a Lord Fauntleroy outfit.

"Why did you look so girlish?" Jill would ask, half amused, half ready to cry.

"Hell and Maria. I don't know why. There should have been a federal law against it. And sissy haircuts too."

At Charlie's urging, he'd wind up, usually, with a tale of his baseball prowess or of the time when he played hooky from school.

"Gee, Dad. Did you do that really?"

With a bit of persuasion, I'd repeat some incident from my big-family childhood. "When I was seven or eight, I turned our playroom into an office with desks, file cabinets and all my younger brothers and sisters as helpers. Four-year-old Billy was the office boy, carrying messages back and forth in a little express cart. We kept frightfully busy."

"Doing what, Mom?"

"Making and selling fancy candy boxes, calendars, penwipers and notebooks. Almost anything and everything."

"Honest?"

"Honest. But one day when all the youngsters kept fighting together, I got mad and fired every one of them. 'And you're fired too,' I told Billy, as he spilled a mess of stuff out of the express cart."

"What happened then?"

"Mother and Dad and my sister Anne came running with buckets of water. 'Where's the fire, Ernie? Where's the fire? Tell us quick?' "

"Even then, Mommy, when you were little, did you love business and want to go into it?"

"Yes . . . I guess I did."

"Ha . . . you're funny."

After Chick had "piggybacked" the kids into bed, we'd kiss them and say good night. "I could eat those little angels," he'd say.

"Me too. I wish they'd stay this age forever."

"What? Remember Jill's to get married at eighteen. If we lived in India, she'd be a bride by now. . . . But

. . . well, she's a darling, isn't she? And that boy Charlie . . ."

Soon he'd begin to discuss today's happenings in his office. "This procedure will mean more work but . . ."

(My mind would wander off to the problem of Charlie bandaging toilet seats.)

"Those new forms will save money eventually . . ."

(His mischief had seemed funny at the beginning. But yesterday when Great-Aunt Agatha received the stuck-fast treatment . . .) "Of course she was furious, Chick. I had to pull and haul; it was awful."

"What was awful?" he'd ask angrily. "Who did you pull and haul? Let's one of us make sense, for Pete's sake."

More frequently, Chick's comments commanded attention and made me tingle. Like an old fire horse, I'd itch to be back in this world of his, weighing the angles and tracing a chain of circumstances to an inevitable conclusion. Yet I knew that we and the children shared something more important now.

"How you love to talk shop," he said one night.

"Why not? Those years of business are a part of me."

"Keep them a part of you."

"Why?"

"Because no experience should ever be wasted. It's come and been met for some reason. If you can't use it one way, shake it well and use it another. Hell, you know what I mean, don't you?"

"I guess so."

After a pep talk like this, he'd turn on the radios full blast (one describing a wrestling match; the other a hockey game) and bury himself in the newspaper. Locked in combat with America's star athletes, he was able to forget business, family cares and aspirations for his wife.

CHAPTER 11

Love Your Neighbor

WHAT is a neighbor?

Until we moved to Manhasset, Chick and I might have described him as a noise and a nuisance, expecting and receiving privacy. During the New York years, we learned to identify him with late parties, suicides and fires. After these flashes of excitement he walked or was carried back into oblivion again.

Once we settled our roots in the country permanently, we began to feel differently. My first conversation with the woman-next-door left a glow that stayed warming. "If you need anything, Mrs. Carey, we're here and most eager to help."

"Thank you."

Several days later she suggested that we urge Jill to stand up for her rights. "A timid child is always bullied by other youngsters, isn't she?"

Chick and I knew very well that everyone must earn respect or be miserable. "If Jill were a boy, Ernie, I'd teach her a haymaker and a left hook."

"For goodness' sakes, teach her anyway."

"No siree."

"Why not? My dad taught the dozen of us to box. I'm pretty good still."

"You take over then, Mrs. Dempsey."

The next afternoon, Jill and I stood toe to toe, exchanging quick jabs and uppercuts. But she hated it. "Let's stop. This is silly."

"She's too gentle," I told Chick. "Why don't you take a flier now?"

But he wouldn't. "If necessary, give her a club. This is your department."

A couple of days later, though, Jill solved her difficulties herself. "We have lemonade at my house usually," she told her tormenters. "And you might be thirsty this afternoon."

Meantime Charlie had been spending his mornings in the back yard. Clambering about his play pen, he was like a fat puppy enjoying the sunshine.

One day when I was scrubbing the bathroom floor, I heard him howl. Rushing through the kitchen, I saw Stephie, a cherubic four-year-old, beating him with a stick.

"Stop, you naughty boy," I cried. "If I catch you, I'll wallop your bottom."

As I was tearing down the street after him, his mother approached in her car. Skidding to a stop, she leaped into the midst of us. "What's going on here?"

Stephie dived toward her skirt. "She's bad."

"He was whacking my baby," I sputtered.

Stephie began to sniffle.

"Did you touch my son?" There was an edge in my neighbor's tone now.

"I itched to, believe me."

"Did she spank you, Stephie? Look at me. Tell Mother."

He came burrowing out, radiant with pride. "She couldn't. I ran too fast."

Friendships have begun, I suppose, under worse handicaps. And thrived under them too, since Charlie gave Stephie's baby brother tit for tat two years later. Anyhow, both families can smile at these shenanigans today.

The bath-of-fire administered by Stephie, and others like him, included our flower beds. Each morning I'd find uprooted pansy plants. By twilight there'd be mayhem among the tulips. Must we set bear traps for these Indians? I'd wonder.

Chick's dismay matched mine. "Why don't parents teach respect for property? Why don't they face up to their responsibilities?"

One evening after he'd been tearing his hair, he received a phone call. "Mr. Carey, I'm your neighbor, Mrs. Hughes . . ."

"Oh yes indeed."

"Has Jill told you what happened to our little magnolia in full bloom?"

"Why no."

"Would you chat with her please . . . and call me back?"

"Certainly. Thank you, Mrs. Hughes."

Setting down the receiver, he looked anything but thankful. "Jill. Oh you, Ji . . . il. Come here immediately."

Since her bedroom door was tightly closed, it took a while for her to hear his summons. Finally she dragged into the kitchen. "Hi, Dad. Want me?"

"It's time you showed up, miss. Do you know a Mrs. Hughes?"

"We . . . met . . . I . . . guess . . . a . . . while . . . ago."

"Speak up so I can hear you. How about her magnolia tree? In full bloom, isn't it?"

"Well . . . yes . . . it was . . . until we played bride there this afternoon."

"Eh?"

"You see . . . on the way home from school it looked pretty . . . so . . . so Susy and I decided to have a wedding."

"A what?"

"First we picked one flower; then the next and the next . . . until there weren't any more."

Chick turned to me. "Are you listening to this, Ern? Imagine such shameful disregard . . ."

"But, Daddy . . . honest, we didn't mean to be bad."

"Tell Mrs. Hughes so, then. I'll go with you." He pushed her ahead of him. "How old are you, Jill? Seven years or seven months?"

They returned soon, almost in tears. But they managed to eat second helpings of supper. And after prayers that night, they were friends again, with grievances forgotten.

"I was sorry for our poor little tyke," Chick told me. "She didn't mean to do wrong. And Mrs. Hughes couldn't have been nicer."

"Bless her."

"She said one thing annoyed her especially though. You see, the kids held their wedding on her newly seeded lawn. Afterwards they tossed flowers and rice all over her porch. It made quite a mess."

"So Jill's learned a lesson?"

He glared a full minute. "Why do you suppose we took that walk tonight? For my health?"

The next afternoon our tulips lay, as usual, in a litter of petals. But as Chick reviewed the damage, he was Mr. Chuckles himself. "Ho. I see somebody's Jill has been in mischief again. Eh? Think I ought to track down the culprit?"

"Of course not, Chick Carey."

"Ho. Did you suppose I was serious? Kids will be kids, won't they?" He began to gather the carnage for his compost heap. "Probably they were playing Red Rover Come Over."

"Or Shoe on the Other Foot," I said. "Size twelve."

Though Chick grew devoted to Mrs. Hughes, he grimaced at the thought of her elderly father. "The blundering old crab," he'd mutter. "The less I see of him the better."

Several months after the magnolia incident, the two men had met for the first time. Since Halloween came on a Sunday that year, Chick had insisted that we observe it then. Even though everyone else in the neighborhood went trick-or-treating the night before.

Dressed in witch and clown outfits, the kids persuaded Daddy to join in the fun. "You were young once upon a time, weren't you?" Jill had wheedled.

The three of them hustled off together and returned laden with spoils. But Chick wasn't the least bit gay. "Never again. Bah."

Jill gave the details later. "Everything was great, Mom, till we got to the very last house. Daddy ran up on the porch and rang the bell. Then some cross old man came out. 'Halloween was last night and you're big enough to know it,' he hollered and slammed the door."

"Next time, you do the chaperoning, Ern," Chick

grumped. "Someone called me a fool tonight. What's more, I agree with him."

One spring evening he received a blast from another neighbor. Dressed in his tennis outfit, he had been whacking balls with a crowd of boys. Tearing across baby grass into a prize dogwood tree, he made a sensational catch. "Have a heart, Mr. Carey," a male voice cried. "If you must be a wild man, stay at your end of the street."

A week later, when he smashed the same man's window, he moved his team to the school grounds. "We can spread out better there. Besides, who wants to be Public Enemy Number One?"

Though Chick became increasingly strict about protecting other people's lawns, he let ours be a playground. "You have to choose between raising kids or grass," he'd say. "Unless you want to go nuts."

Children playing outdoors, he thought, were fine. But hordes of them trooping through the house drove him crazy. Especially after a hard day at the office. "Why must these youngsters we don't know take over here?" he'd ask as treasure hunters swarmed in and stripped us of shoelaces, matchboxes and spools of thread. "If they have homes of their own, why don't they do their high jinks there?"

Fortunately, on Jill's next birthday celebration, he was out of town. Otherwise he would have learned *why*, as I did.

As usual she had planned the menu and entertainment herself, shopping favors at the dime store. When our dozen guests had gulped down their hamburgers, corn, ice cream and Coca-Cola, she announced the next big event: *treasure hunt.* The oddments to be collected included a cigar wrapper, a 1935 penny and a strand of bright-red hair.

Because of the hair, the girls had an unusually trying night. Only one family, many blocks away, could supply this pearl of great price. Aware that the very hairs of their heads were numbered, the Kerleys refused to part with any.

Mr. Kerley, in his carrot-topped glory, met the first team of hunters with no pleasure. "Go away, kids, won't you? My wife and a couple of the boys are sick. I've had a bad day already."

"But please . . ."

As the second team arrived, five of the Kerley children came clustering about their father. Next the two others joined the group in their pajamas. Beaming, they began to pluck at each other's scalps.

"No you don't," their father commanded. "You two get back to bed this minute."

Jill's team approached now, swarming up on the veranda. "Hi, Mr. Kerley-wurley."

Backing away, he placed his hands over his eyes. "I tell you No. My wife is sick and . . ."

A chorus of protests rose piteously. "But look, it means just a teeny-tiny yank . . ."

After slippers had scuffed down the stairs, Mrs. Kerley appeared in her bathrobe. "I'm sorry to interfere . . . but we must be kind." Lifting some shears to her hair, she snipped briskly. "Here you are, girls."

"Why must we put up with this nonsense?" Mr. Kerley grumped. "I tell you, Clara, it's an imposition."

"Next time I'll keep my list simpler," Jill told me later. "Tonight was too mixed up — sort of."

The morning after Jill's party, Charlie decided it was his turn to offer hospitality. When he had selected the same hamburger-ice cream bill of fare, he invited his friend Sandy for supper and the night.

In the late afternoon, Mrs. Davis came down the street with her son and his suitcase. "If he gets homesick, Ern, remember we're just two houses away. This is his first visit away from us ever."

Until bedtime, our guest had a beautiful time. After splashing in the bathtub with Charlie, he got into his pajamas and kissed us good night.

With the children settled, Chick and I sat on the front stoop, watching the first star appear. Behind us a faint bleating rose to a roar. "I want my mother. I want my mother." Plunging past us, Sandy ran home.

"He didn't like it here," Charlie explained.

Incidents like these drew us toward our neighbors. Increasingly, the barriers built in New York kept crumbling away. Yet this was a hide-and-seek thing, this new sense of companionship and closeness. "I meant to be friendly before now," a young mother confided. "But you seemed to be busy. And I didn't know how to begin."

This had been our trouble too: not knowing how to begin. But we were learning.

Month after month, simple gestures came spontaneously: gifts of garden flowers, pot holders and hot cross buns. There was the grandmotherly friend who insisted, "You plan on a spree tomorrow; I'll watch the children.". . . And the man across the street who turned off our water, preventing a flood. . . . And the folks next door who kept us overnight when our furnace pooped out.

"Honestly, Ernie," Chick said again and again, "did you ever see such kindness?"

Then one morning, near tragedy came without warning. Charlie had been thrown from his tricycle onto the street.

We kept him there, the neighbors and I, until the doctor arrived and examined him. "He's sound from head to toe, Mrs. Carey. But I'd keep him quiet for a couple of days."

"Thank you," we said, bowing our heads.

CHAPTER 12

Do It Yourself

SOME people insist on sharing every moment of wonder and beauty. Chick is this way. If the sunset is breathtaking, he drags us out to see it. When the first leaf fans into shape, we must come running. If a bird tweet-tweets, the world stops until we find and identify the little sprite. Maybe this is another New England carry-over. Anyhow it is pure Carey.

"Your ignorance floors me, Ernie," he keeps saying. "How can a grown woman know so little about nature?"

This lack of tact never fails to make me explode. Yet it is true that none of us Gilbreths knows, or wishes to know, a flicker from a nuthatch. Our feathered friends may be God's marvelous creatures, but we prefer them at a distance. "Birdie, birdie on the tree. Let not your droppings drop on me!"

Chick can tell you, and will, that birds are separate personalities. For example, a mother robin may insist during pregnancy that her mate bring special tidbits. Afterwards she has no taste for them. "Temperamental, by golly, like all females."

In spare moments he keeps scanning the skies or stringing suet temptingly. And if we own no cats here in Manhasset, there are reasons beyond my dislike for them.

My curiosity about astronomy and ants is an outgrowth of my father's teachings. Though Chick takes the universe in stride, he considers ants to be no better than termites, black widow spiders and the bubonic plague. "What's good about those pests? Who cares whether they keep slaves or use them as food barrels? Get up off your stomach now, while I administer some boiling water."

"Don't. Don't," I cry. "They're here for some good reason."

"Well, they're not here any longer, damn it."

Though we argue continually on these matters, all of us Careys love flowers. The first crocus brings a giddy moment which we share together. "Nice, isn't it?" we say. "I hope nobody kicks this to blazes now."

"We have the prettiest garden in the entire world," Jill used to say as the daffodils, violets and peonies came in sequence. "But tulips are the best," Charlie chorused.

From tuliptime on, Chick and I struggled to achieve green thumbs. Though the children liked helping to order seeds from the catalogue, they were allergic to spades and shovels. "Sorry, folks. Got to be going," they'd call back over their shoulders.

Do It Yourself

During our first year in Manhasset, Chick kept surveying the back yard sadly. "Who can grow anything in this two-bit space? With a couple of acres I could go berserk, darn it."

By our second spring we managed to lease some land half a mile away. Soon Chick spent every spare moment there, trudging back and forth with his wheelbarrow and tools. At supper he'd be radiant. "You should see those radishes; up an eighth of an inch at least."

At such times I'd choke back the comment that none of us ate radishes or kohlrabi or kale or parsnips bought in the large-sized seed packet.

Eventually the rest of us followed him like sheep every night. After weeding a bit, we'd eat a picnic supper. Then singing "Our Highland Goat" in three-part harmony, we'd wind back home.

While he hovered over his vegetables, I experimented with flowers. Mixing manure with chemicals, ingenuity with faith, I broke every gardening rule. "You'll see I'm right too," I promised.

After a gloomy experience with sweet peas, Chick made a point of ignoring Mme. Burbank. One February I had persuaded him to dig a six-foot trench for the seeds. Since the ground was frozen stiff, this chore took several weeks. Afterwards there wasn't a single sprout.

Chick kept examining his handiwork and shaking his head. Then when he had checked the seed packet he glared. "This says dig a trench six inches. Hell and Maria, you had me halfway to China. Oh, my aching back!"

After the sweet-pea tragedy, I bought a large can of Expando. The advertisement, with garish before-and-after pictures, promised that "blooms would bust out all over, creating a real Paradise." You're my dish, I thought, ordering the five-gallon economy-size treatment."

Two weeks after the first application, there was no noticeable response. So following a hunch, I tripled the dose. Overnight the plants leafed, bloomed and spread wildly. "Hold it. *Hoooold it,*" I warned as the pansies blew up like monster balloons. "Take it easy, for gracious sakes."

"You're bucking Mother Nature," Chick warned. "She'll bite you back."

"A cocktail was what she needed. I bet she loves this."

But evidently the old girl didn't love it. Two weeks later, my flowers lay flat, their giant faces a picture of sorrow. "One, two, three, *out,*" Chick said merrily. "Didn't I say this would happen?"

At times like this, I wondered why I had married this man. Or endured his attempts at humor. "If you want sympathy, look in the dictionary, honey child; under the letter *S.*" Phooey.

Though I bought and used other chemicals as they were advertised, I had no use for old-fashioned compost.

Unsightly and smelling dank, it almost made me sick. "Why don't you get rid of that witches' brew, Chick?"

"No farmer would think of wasting this precious stuff."

"But we're not farmers."

"You're not, obviously. But I'm trying to be one."

Whenever he found a dead mole, bird or mouse, he'd fling it into his precious heap. "From nothing we make *this,*" he'd say, drooling over the elixir for next year's crop.

"It's a graveyard," I'd moan.

He kept policing the kitchen to be sure that no bit of lettuce or carrot skin was wasted. "Save that for my pile."

It annoyed me. "Stop being a Shylock. You'll heave the children and me in there next."

"You'd come out cleansed in body and soul."

"And minus our heads, I bet."

Another touchy subject was Chick's vigor with the pruning shears. Tackling everything but the loftiest trees, he resembled a wind storm. Afterwards, picking my way through fallen bodies and limbs, I'd wail, "What are you doing, you madman? Stop. Please stop."

Yet Nature responded to the rough treatment, rewarding him with blooms as never before. Regardless, I winced whenever he began this routine. Woodman, spare that tree!

Except for the pleasure of raking leaves and shoveling snow, we would have preferred to skip the cold seasons of the year. Indoor tasks postponed until now made fall and winter particularly disagreeable. Locks would have to be fixed, plaster patched and walls repainted. Why, we wondered, did home ownership and a tight budget bring such pettiness?

After spending two days trying to fix a faucet, Chick yelled, "A pox on this thing. I'm no Ph.D. plumber." Then in later weeks as he struggled with a hammer, "Why did we ever ensnare ourselves in this house? The sooner it falls apart the better."

Though we managed to take down the screens by December, the storm windows stayed in the cellar. "Who needs them, anyway? We won't freeze to death."

It took us a month to paper the bathroom; even then the design wasn't straight. We fussed with solder and burned ourselves. We fumed and wished we lived in an apartment. We watched our neighbors zipping up and down ladders, working power saws and repairing electrical equipment expertly. Unvanquished still, we asked ourselves, "Am I clumsy or was I born retarded?"

We redecorated the kitchen finally . . . after a disheartening experience. Charlie had been leaving apple cores everywhere during this period; and one lay on the cellar steps as Chick started down them with a gallon of paint.

Skidding, he slammed the can against the banisters and clung there. "Eeooow, Ernie," he howled as gray ooze flooded his head and neck. "Come quick. I'm drowning."

"You've just thrown six dollars all over yourself," I said angrily.

"I know. Look at me. Good God."

"Oh dear. Well, let's salvage what we can." I handed him a brush. "And if you want sympathy, look in the dictionary . . ."

After he had painted his way down into the basement, he stood glaring at me. "How do I get back upstairs now, Miss Bright-eyes? If you think I'm going to stay imprisoned here . . ."

Finally he came leaping toward me, leaving huge footprints in his wake. But he was grinning. "This makes me think of some vaudeville years ago. Or maybe it was a Keystone comedy. Anyhow, there were two fool workmen . . ."

"Tripping over planks? And banging each other with pails?"

"Yes. That was the one." We stood chuckling in spite ourselves.

"Don't feel too badly, Chick."

"Hell and Maria. I don't feel badly. Only once we get this dratted, godforsaken, benighted kitchen finished, I'll never touch a paintbrush again. Or a chisel or a hammer or a nail."

"Good. Me too."

Previous owners of our home evidently were charter members of the Do It Yourself fraternity. Needless electric sockets, shelves and gadgets had been installed in every room. Most baffling of all, the cellar had a vast spiderweb of wires hanging at nose level. "We'll get rid of that hazard some day," Chick promised. "Even a monkey couldn't learn to avoid it."

An errand in the cellar always bruised and scarred us. "Guillotined again," we'd announce cheerily.

Eventually we accepted our danger zone as a sort of beloved old joke. "Darn Boob McNutt brain wave," Chick would say proudly.

Though the kids had no enthusiasm for gardening, they became skilled with a paintbrush and hammer. When our walls needed refinishing, Jill mixed the shade and applied it expertly. When Chick failed to fix the handle of a door, Charlie clicked it and made it work. "What's so hard about this?" they'd ask, as we stood open-mouthed.

"Either they're Einsteins or we're morons," Chick would say. "And they're not Einsteins."

"I'll decorate my desk green next," Jill said happily, "with a gold stripe and a bunch of buttercups somewhere."

"Next time buy bigger nails, Dad," Charlie suggested. "We got to do this *right*, you know."

But when the first crocus appeared each year, the children paused less and less. "Sorry, folks . . . got to be going . . ."

"They're scared sick of outside chores," Chick murmured, shaking his head. "I'll be damned."

"I know. I can't understand them."

"Sssh, Ernie. Isn't that a robin up there? Ssssh. Listen."

CHAPTER 13

Come and Be Young Again

My fondness for children, the more the merrier, has always puzzled Chick. To me, home should be a sort of clubhouse with doors slamming, footsteps clambering everywhere, the singing of several songs all at once, acrobatics, arguments, crumbs being spilled and no minute ever twice the same. "This way," I tell Chick, "we have the fun of a big family. Only we don't have to worry about shoes-by-the-gross, food bills or countless college educations."

This statement always makes him yodel at the top of his lungs, "Thank the Lord for *that* blessing at least."

When the uproar grows unbearable on Saturday afternoons, he has a way of standing at attention and counting our guests. "Thirty," he says, without bothering to lower his voice. "Can't these hooligans meet somewhere else occasionally? Have you seen how they've wrecked the kitchen?"

"Why worry? We can repaint it one of these days."

"Hell and Maria. Don't suggest such torture."

Between these occasional protests, he has always showered hospitality and attention on our youngsters' chums. "Want some more cookies, kids, or some bread with butter and sugar? Is anyone thirsty for lemonade?" Then as everyone swarms around him, "Take it easy. Take it easy. One at a time."

Now and again he has urged Becky or Jim to bring a favorite pet to call. "Next time be sure to bring that superintelligent rabbit along. . . . If that crow is what you say he is, he ought to be a college professor instead of a bird. Anyhow, I want to see him."

Then after youngsters had taken pains to comply, he'd say sorrowfully, "So now, Ernie, in addition to everything else, they drag their livestock in here. Good God. What next?"

"But Chick . . . you . . ."

"Did I? Then I must be a dodo."

Yet during the animal and bird exhibitions, he enjoyed himself thoroughly. And why not? Snowball, as Becky had promised, was a marvelous creature, enormous, belligerent, beautiful. He somersaulted for carrots, winked and did a sort of lumbering fox trot in perfect rhythm. "What a character," Chick whispered, deeply impressed. "Makes our old Houdini, years ago, look like the flathead he was."

Mr. Crow's tricks, flapping and jigging to a harmonica, seemed less memorable than his lax habits. "Who's going to clean up after him?" Jill asked hopefully later. "You, Charlie?"

"No. He's *your* friend, isn't he?"

"He was. But not any more, darn it."

"Hasn't someone got a trained horse to exhibit here too?" Chick asked bitterly. "He might be better behaved."

"If you're interested, Dad," Jill promised, "we'll hunt around and see."

"Don't do me any favors."

"One minute you like something, Daddy. The next you don't. I just can't figure you out."

"All I want around here is a little peace and quiet sometimes."

"But wouldn't that be awfully boring?"

"I don't know. So far, there hasn't been a chance to find out."

When Jill became a Brownie, her interest in club meetings and animals evaporated. "That was baby stuff," she told us. "Just too, too dreary. Now I must do my best to love God and my country; to help other people every day, especially those at home. And you must do your best too, Mom, since you're a leader."

"Leader?" Chick asked, looking as though she had dubbed me Queen Guinevere. "When the devil did this happen . . . and why?"

"Well, in order to form this troop, honey . . . another mother and I . . . she's carrying the real responsibility . . ."

"But you were never in Scouts, were you? What do you know about it?"

"I've been reading up on it. All you need is 'sincerity of interest and understanding.' You try to make 'this first group experience a happy one for all.' "

"For the fathers too?"

"Yes. Of course."

After several Brownie meetings at the school, it was clear that our dozen little ones had another leader their own age. Saintly faced, with old-fashioned braids, Sybil had the fire of a Viking. She'd groan whenever we suggested bean-bag play or craft work. Then her followers would chant, "It's boring. Let's do something else."

Finally we gave an elaborate pantomime with Sybil playing the king. From this moment on, she was our vcry bcst hclpcr.

"You should have made her feel Big Girl sooner," Jill chided. "If we hold the meetings in our house, Mom, and forget dumb games and nature walks, it will be super."

After several sessions in our kitchen, the Brownies became wing-dings at cookie, cake and pie making. Like the elves in the fairy tale, they hopped and danced about, working swiftly. They managed to eat whatever they made, even if it was like granite. "We baked this a little too much," they'd say, grinding their teeth.

Adoringly, they saved souvenirs of their prowess for Chick. "Try this, Mr. Carey. Try this. We made it ourselves. Isn't it delicious?"

Manfully, he'd take a taste and choke. Then a dozen pairs of legs would race to get him some water.

"Must we go through this routine every week?" he'd groan afterwards. "It's ruining my stomach."

"But the girls are trying to be generous."

"Generous? With that horrible handout? Even a dog couldn't digest it."

"Of course they *love* cooking. But maybe we can interest them in sewing."

"Do, for Pete's sake. Start them mending some of my socks."

"You mean . . . ? Oh Chick. I've been forgetful. I'm so sorry."

"Don't be sorry. Only get those girls doing something more constructive. For the sake of my health."

Meantime, day after day, Jill kept living her Brownie promise about "helping loved ones at home." She made her bed frequently, left less of a clutter and dried the dishes. "Do you want your pipe, Daddy dear? Or your slippers?"

"What's eating that child, Ern? Is she sick?"

"She's doing a good deed."

"Tell her to good-deed somebody else then. She makes me nervous."

Soon Jill found richer fields for *service* in Charlie. "Don't slop all over the floor, honey," she'd say as he spilled some milk. "It isn't kind."

He paid no attention.

She'd rush to wipe up the mess. "I can bend easier than you. Can't I, Mom?"

"You're goony, Jill," he'd crow without looking up. "Why are you so goony?"

"I won't answer him back," she'd mutter to herself. "Or smack him either. But oh, I'd like to!"

After several months in Manhasset, I had become a Sunday School teacher. Though Chick considered this development unbelievable, I loved being with my crowd of three-year-olds. "Hi," they'd say, slamming past toward the sandbox as they arrived.

When Charlie joined our group the following year, bedlam broke loose. Jill, who had seen some of his high jinks one morning, described them to Chick. "He was in mischief every minute, Daddy. You should have seen him."

With hair still slickly combed and suit immaculate, our son smiled winningly. "Don't believe her. Don't believe her."

"You know you wouldn't let any of the other kids

near Mother or the sandbox," Jill scolded. "You kept hitting them and shouting, 'You get away.' "

"Did you do that, Charles?" Chick asked in his most serious tone.

Charlie nodded.

"Why?"

Rolling his eyes, he debated his answer silently.

"You really were very selfish," I said, deeply annoyed still. "Since you're such a baby, maybe you belong home. . . ."

"O.K., Mommy," he spoke at last, completely content with the situation.

"No you don't, Ernie," Chick broke in. "No you don't. That boy needs religious education. What's more . . . I need him to need it."

"Daddy's the boss," Charlie said, gravely. "Like he says, *we* need it. Eh, Dad?"

Meantime we had been drawn into ever-closer communion with Jill's school. From first grade on, there had been parent-briefing sessions where we absorbed new methods of teaching. Yet the discussion periods which followed were always more illuminating. We'd be neck-deep in word-reading, when some father would ask, "My Johnny keeps scratching himself at home. Does he do this at school?"

Or brooding about the goal behind discipline, we'd

hear someone say agitatedly, "Many of us mothers do not approve of dungarees. Yet my Mary insists . . ."

"I've done my duty . . . but I'm crippled for life," Chick would say when we got home. "Those blasted chairs should be bigger . . . or next time you'll have to drag me there."

"Didn't my desk look neat last night, Dad?" Jill would ask proudly the next morning. "Didn't you love my teacher? . . . And don't you wish you were a schoolboy all over again?"

"To questions one and two, honey, definitely Yes. For the rest . . . Hell and Maria *No.* I'd rather be tarred and feathered, alive and kicking."

"But why?"

After catching himself, Chick spoke more carefully. "Let's see why. For one thing, when you hacked around or didn't pay attention years ago, you got a ruler. Hard across the wrist."

"But were *you* that way much?"

"Now and again, I guess I was. But times and teachers have changed since then. And I've grown up some too."

Jill looked at her wrist broodingly. "They must have been really cruel to little boys long, *long ago.* Weren't they?"

Questions about my early schooling brought equally vehement answers. "I wouldn't endure a minute of it again either. You see, the dozen of us Gilbreths grew up under the very same teachers . . ."

"Why was that so awful, Mom?"

I went into a lugubrious imitation. "Too bad you're not better in arithmetic, dear. Anne was such a whiz. Too bad you're such a dolt at geography, dear. Too bad . . ."

"But with only one older sister, didn't you come off fairly easy?"

"No, because Anne was a brilliant student always . . . very best in the family."

"Times are hard all over," Chick said chuckling. "We'd better get out the dictionary and open it at *S*."

"You do that," I promised, "and I'll *really* get upset."

Though, like most fathers, Chick was unable to attend morning or afternoon school activities, he enjoyed hearing about them. Especially when Jill played a key role or won a dance-costume prize.

"Today I was Dorothy in the *Wizard of Oz*," she'd say at supper. "It was neat except that the curtains went wild in the last act and kept banging back and forth. Then at the end, the rainbow missed us by a couple of miles."

"Who minds a little trouble like that?" Chick would ask comfortingly.

"It didn't bother us really. Only with everyone yack-yacking, you can't help feeling sort of silly."

"Don't I know," Chick said. "Something similar happened to me in my first-and-last school performance." His cheeks grew red. "I was the personification of Spring, all dolled up in a green union suit. About fifteen of the biggest girls in our class were trees: the spirit of Maple, Birch, Evergreen and such." He took a deep, painful breath. "At the big moment I was supposed to come leaping on stage: 'Awake, my sleeping beauties. Arise. Arise.' "

Jill choked back a giggle.

"But, damn it, I fumbled my cue . . . and came leaping and shouting way ahead of schedule. Oweeeee!"

"And what happened then?"

"I guess they had to carry me off on a stretcher."

"Poor Daddy. Why does it matter so much still?"

He looked at her blankly. "I wish to heavens I knew."

Perhaps Chick's skill in dancing made him tantalized by Jill's afterschool classes. He never seemed to hear enough about new steps. And he built real admiration for Miss Baldwin, the teacher, a sort of Dresden-doll creature, loaded with ruffles and the patience of Job.

Miss Baldwin's big moment each year was the party where she awarded prizes for costumes. She insisted on one rule only: each creation must be homemade. "Lucky you, Ernie," Chick would say, glancing at me sympathetically. "You enjoy this, I know, like a blow on the head."

In most Manhasset homes, once the date for the party had been announced, mothers went into a frenzy of sewing, painting, embroidering and goodness knows what. Meantime their families ate canned goods, left-overs and store-bought cake. "Mother's so busy fixing sparkles on my Snow Queen costume," a young guest would tell us at dinner, "that it's pathetic. Honestly."

Fortunately for the Careys, Jill never remembered to relay news of the party until the last minute. "Guess what," she'd say cheerfully, "tomorrow's the big bang-out. We'll hustle around and fix me something fast."

"But why did you wait until now, dear? There's not a rag in the house."

"Don't worry. We'll find something. We always do."

To Chick's delight, our most successful done-in-desperation outfit was entitled "Washday." "Did you really win two prizes in that horror?" he asked his daughter, after she strutted by in a torn pillowcase, four clothes-pins and some heavy line.

Jill nodded glumly. "They said I was the funniest and the most original. Murder! If only I could have been a fairy instead . . . or something beautiful."

"Next time, if you don't give more notice, you can go in your petticoat," I said, deeply hurt.

"As long as it's a pretty petticoat, Mom, I'd much *rather* . . ."

"While we're on the subject of public appearances,"

Chick would say at a time like this, "wasn't that costume today a little too brief? It seemed so scanty and tight."

"But, good Lord, Chick, why not? Jill's only eight . . ."

"She's a girl, nevertheless. And she should be raised with all the proprieties . . ."

Charlie would listen to us all with eyes like saucers.

"But, Chick . . ."

"Now you listen to me, Ernie . . ."

"Daddy, stop being so prudish," Jill would say, dancing toward him. "Remember, this is 1946."

"It happens that you're my daughter."

"Don't you want me to be like the other kids? If I'm not, how can I ever get married some day?"

"What in thunder has *that* got to do with *this*?"

"Everything. What was Mother like when you met her?"

After thinking a minute, he cleared his throat. "She was very much a lady; of that you may be sure. Say, what color dress did you have on that night, Ern? Wasn't it red?"

CHAPTER 14

Reunion in Nantucket

AFTER two summers in Long Island, Chick agreed to spend our next holiday in Nantucket, Massachusetts. "But a tent would be less primitive than that dear old Gilbreth cottage."

"Maybe the beds aren't comfortable," I admitted, "and those low beams keep you stooping, of course. Still, I'm homesick . . . going back again will seem good."

"Remember, we kids have never seen The Shoe and those wobbly old lighthouses," Jill cried. "I just can't wait. Can you, Charlie?"

"Nope."

"But this year I need two weeks of rest," Chick kept protesting throughout the next months.

"You'll get them," I promised, "except for the first day and night. My brothers' and sisters' vacations won't overlap with ours. We all worked it out very carefully."

He shook his head. "When one Gilbreth is in Nantucket, every Gilbreth is in Nantucket. I love the crowd of you . . . but in smaller doses."

"There won't be a pile-up this time, though. In fact, I bet you'll be lonely as an owl."

"Ho. When I see it, I'll believe it."

Though Chick had been through an unusually strenuous year, this attitude surprised me. Did he really want a quiet vacation? What had happened to Charles-the-nature-boy, who kept us Gilbreths dancing? Had he forgotten his love of this island off the coast of Massachusetts and the sport it offered?

In the past, hadn't he wakened us at dawn always, for a swim and a game of Pep-up? Didn't he keep us hurtling through beach picnics, blueberry-picking expeditions and treks miles away for ginger ice cream? Swapping yarns and shaggy-dog stories in dialect, didn't he refuse to let us go to bed? "Don't show the white feather, folks. Stick around a while."

Yet now in the drama of more vivid recollections, he seemed to forget all this. For example, he'd speak of that first summer at The Shoe soon after our marriage. At my insistence he had thrust himself between two battling young towheads. "Cut it out, boys. Do you want to kill each other?"

"Sure. Who are you to try and stop us?"

Though Freddy and Dan were friends again immediately, they ignored Chick for the rest of the day. "And no wonder," I said, siding with them. "It was a Gilbreth affair. Strictly Gilbreth."

"Of course. So why did you keep hollering, 'Please, Chick, make them stop'?"

"I was scared, I suppose. But now I can't blame the boys for blaming you."

"Hell and Maria," he said, blinking. "I'll never understand you or your family. Ever."

"Blood is thicker than in-laws, honey."

"Have you forgotten I'm your husband?"

Since the children had never been to Nantucket, Chick took pains to explain what they would find there. "As our steamer passes the jetty, you'll see the most beautiful bathing beach in the world. A block or so away, walking distance, is the cottage and the two lighthouses your Granddaddy Gilbreth bought in 1918. The place has an interesting history, because originally The Shoe was half its present size and used as a storehouse for oil. The towers were channel markers, placed so that the old whalers could keep their ships from going aground."

"What's it like inside, Dad?"

"Let's see. The furniture reminds me of our vacations years ago in New Hampshire. Except for the beds, darn it, which are the worst I've ever slept in. Your grandparents' interest in science and Morse code and time-and-motion saving is clear everywhere. Even on the walls and ceilings. You'll find yourselves learning bits of information when you wake up in the morning and stretch."

"Ha. Like what?"

"Code symbols, for example. Like this: A: dot dash; B: dash dot dot dot. Until you get dotty."

"That ought to be fun. Now how about the towers?"

"Well, they flank the cottage on either side, just a few yards away. The little one is called Mic, the big one Cyc, for reasons the Gilbreths refuse to make public. Mic is two stories high, Cyc three; and from the outside they're cute as bugs. Inside, though . . ." he frowned and went more slowly now, "there are winding stairs round and round and round, and platforms wide enough to hold cots." Turning to me, he raised his voice. "And if you or your family ever asks me to sleep in that hellhole again *ever*, I promise you I won't."

Oh dear, I thought. Why can't he forget that experience in Cyc years ago? Must that awful night haunt him eternally?

Wakened by the blasts of a northeaster, we had stumbled down the stairs to the ground floor. Since electric lights had gone off and we were unable to force open the outside door, we clung together in the heaving, creaking cradle-of-the-deep. "I've never been seasick in my life," Chick groaned, careening back and forth. "But . . . I'm . . . going . . . to . . . be . . . now. Ooops."

When a lull came at last, we managed to fight our

way back to the cottage. Since everyone was sleeping serenely there, we sat through the rest of the storm, drinking coffee and nursing our nerves.

"Good morning, landlubbers," my brothers chanted as they awoke one by one. "Imagine finding you pantywaists here."

Chick pulled his blanket more tightly around his shoulders. "Listen, you hotshots. When I die, I don't want to be rocked to blazes first. In your lighthouse or anywhere else."

"In Nantucket we ignore a little blow like this. It's tradition."

"Ho. Don't give me that malarkey."

Resolutely, year after year, Frank, Bill, Fred, Dan, Jack and Bob kept trying to mold him to their pattern. One noon, with the air of conferring a knighthood, two of them asked him to crew in a Yacht Club race. "Maybe you've never sailed a sloop before, chum, but it's time you learned."

Though the boys achieved first place that day, Chick couldn't have been less enthusiastic. "Never again, Ernie. Those young demons sent me into the innards of that old scow and kept me there. It was one command after another. "Act alive; give her more slack. Haul her in, you so and so; haul her in." I never once got my nose out of that godforsaken, stinking hole. Peuw."

"You have to be bossy when you're captaining a boat,"

I explained. "Otherwise you'd never get clear of the mooring."

"Peuw," he repeated.

Jill and Charlie always appreciated these stories more than I could. "Did our uncles really treat you so mean?" they'd ask delightedly.

"Sure. If they'd shanghaied me, it couldn't have been worse."

"But you won the blue flag that day, didn't you?"

"They did. I was the benighted also-ran."

My memories of Nantucket were never as sharp as Chick's. Perhaps the sunshine flooding them tended to be blinding. Anyhow, sand, beach grass and sky seemed to meld into a haze of pale pinks, green and purest blue. This was what I liked to recall: a picture cherished from girlhood, forever fresh and serene.

"I can't believe we're going back there," I crooned as we stowed our vacation gear into a taxi at last. "Aren't you tickled now we're on our way?"

After whistling for Winnie, our new puppy, he placed her in Charlie's arms. "Watch this little vixen now, for goodness' sakes, will you? She's your responsibility . . . not mine."

"How about it, Dad?" Jill said, as he paused to wipe his brow. "As Mommy says, aren't you tickled?"

"Ask me two weeks from now. Humph! Why did we ever get into this folderol? It wasn't my idea."

Whenever any of us Gilbreths approached Nantucket Island by steamer, we stood clustered on the upper deck near the captain's quarters. Smiling and waving handkerchiefs wildly, we exchanged salutes with the family welcoming committees: one on a dune near The Shoe, another on the rocks surrounding Brant Point, still another on the wharf.

"Hello. Hello," we Careys hooted now, identifying our kin. "How are you, Bill . . . and Dan? What's the score here? How's the sailing and fishing?" Next we were in the midst of hugs, kisses and slaps on the back. Then we climbed into one of the cars, squeezed ourselves between endless luggage and children and headed for home.

As we drove up to the weatherbeaten front door, everything looked exactly as it should. Flapping overhead as always, the American flag waved its greeting. "Hi," we cried to it and the bathing-suit brigade gripping our shoulders and waists. "Hi. Good to see you. My, you look tan."

"Come in, palefaces. Chick, we're putting you and Ern in Cyc, for old times' sake. You kids will sleep on the porch here."

Chick paused long enough to scan the heavens for signs of a northeaster. Seeing none, he was able to keep smiling. "We're stuck, Ern," he whispered to me. "Never mind. Let's get off these infernal city clothes. What are we waiting for?"

In [illegible]ng hours while the Gilbreths wound up their vacations, we reveled in the old eat-swim-and-be-merry routine. With Chick our self-elected leader, we never once caught our breaths. "Shake yourselves," he insisted, when we were too weary to move. "Let's take a moonlight swim, you zombies."

"Jeepers, Chick," my brothers protested. "Where did you get this steam?"

"Why not enjoy what we have here? Man oh man."

After the swim, which no one but Chick enjoyed especially, we sat until dawn, exchanging stories and yacks. "Don't be a wet blanket," he wailed, as one by one we dragged off to bed. "Why poop out? You're only young once."

"Sorry, Tarzan. But I'm dead on my feet. Good night."

In reviewing that all-too-brief reunion later, we Careys agreed that it was blissful. Except for one complication: dogs. And our dog, most particularly.

It was Dan who discovered Winnie squatting on Mother's brand-new grass rug. "Hey, stupit, not in the living room," he howled, imitating the old hired man who had helped to raise us and our pets. "Hey, *out*, before I smack you *good*." Then, as Winnie finished her business and tried to lick his hands, "No you don't, you bold thing, you."

"Winnie-the-Pooh has a new name now," Bill chortled, "and the privileges thereto: Miss Rug-Pooh Carey."

Then slipping into Dan's dialect he put his nose close to hers. "You're in there a thousant per cent, ain't you, Rug-Pooh?"

She showed her appreciation by nipping his ear.

"I guess I asked for it," he said cheerfully.

"She's never acted this way before . . . very often," I murmured. "Please excuse her."

Miss Rug-Pooh developed other quirks which hadn't been evident before . . . very often. She tore the trousers of the postman, milkman and garbageman. She dived at the children, especially the toddlers. She stole tidbits from the kitchen and the dining room. And she developed a hate for Dan's police dog, Bonnie.

"Why do you keep that animal?" someone asked us.

"Darned if we know."

"Maybe she needs a psychiatrist."

"If this nonsense keeps up, we'll all need one."

In contrast, Bonnie's behavior stayed bonnie. Watching her *p*'s and *q*'s like Emily Post, she ignored our mosquito-sized vixen. With her ears and tail utterly flat, she'd place her head on Dannie's knee. Woe. A thousand times woe.

"Never mind, baby," he'd soothe, patting her flanks. "Never mind."

"I feel badly about this," I kept saying.

"Don't die over it, Ernie. We know you *tried* to raise her right."

"It was a mistake to bring Winnie here," I said to Chick. "I'm sure no one can love us for it."

He nodded.

"What's Mother going to say when she sees those spots on her rug?"

"She'll know I'm not guilty, at least. Long ago I voted against a dog, didn't I?"

"Yes. Even when Charlie told you, 'She'll be littler than me, Dad. She'll come running when I say come,' you weren't the least bit swayed."

"Why would I be? One of us, at least, had to hold out and be sensible."

"Maybe so. But now you love Winnie more than we do."

"Ho. I do? Who says so?" Without realizing it, he'd lean over and pat her. "Wuzza, wuzza. Pretty girl."

Before the Gilbreths departed by steamer and plane, we had a last chat together. "You Careys may not have the quiet time you're hoping for here," Dan warned, rolling his eyes. "Excursion buses come by since The Shoe's become an island landmark. And, well, sight-seers haunt this place."

"Oh no."

"Of coursc we all love seeing old friends when they drop in. But most of these callers are strangers with time on their hands."

"Gad," Chick said, horror-stricken.

"Unless you intend to be Glad Hand Charlie, the official greeter," Bill advised, "I'd duck off to the beach early. Take a picnic lunch."

"Or hit for the ocean and drown yourself," Dan added.

"Oh," I sighed. "Oh."

"We've been mistaken for every one of you Gilbreth girls," my sisters-in-law sputtered. " 'Hello, dear, you're Andie, aren't you? You aren't? Then you must be Ernestine. Then you must be Martha or Lillian.' "

"I've been called Frank fifty times at least," Bill said. "Now I keep asking myself, 'Who the devil am I?' "

"Well, who are you?" his wife demanded. "Maybe I'd better make sure too."

"My name used to be William, sister Anne."

"In other words," I said, frowning at my brothers, "we're sure to be driven daffy here."

"Indeed yes, Lillian."

"Carambo," I moaned, avoiding Chick's glance.

"That goes for you too, Fred; I mean Jack," they told him.

"If you fellows were able to live through it, I guess I can," he said gamely.

"Hell, Chick. Believe me, we're beat. In a way, it's a relief to be leaving today."

"I won't let this lick me," he promised, squaring his shoulders.

"That's the old spirit," they hooted. "Keep smiling, you jay bird."

"Awk. Awk. Awk," he croaked, flapping his arms.

"Well, so long, Frank; excuse me . . . Bob," they said, shaking hands warmly. "Hope to run into you again next summer. Remember me to your remarkable mother. There's only *one* Dr. Gilbreth."

"This isn't the least bit funny," I scolded.

"Rest your features, Martha," Bill said, ducking. "Oh excuse me, who could guess you are Jane?"

"It's high comedy maybe," I admitted. "But don't overplay it."

"Look, Ernie. We're just trying to warn you."

"Thanks. Thanks a million."

"Golly, I hate to see everyone go," Chick said as the last contingent of Gilbreths went off waving. "What will we do in this morgue by ourselves now? Golly."

"At last we can sit down and catch our breaths. It feels good too, doesn't it?"

He looked at me in utter astonishment. "Who wants to rest and relax?"

"Don't you, Chick? Didn't you insist . . . ?"

"Ho. Maybe I felt that way before we got here. But" — he whacked my back so hard that it hurt — "this is our *vacation,* honey. Hip, hip, hooray!"

CHAPTER 15

Whale Ahoy

WITH population at The Shoe reduced to a mere four now, Winnie began to correct her manners. But her fondness for Mother's rug and Chick's resurgence of energy continued to be problems. And protesting to dog and man accomplished nothing. "Better save your breath," Jill told me. "Anyway, they don't hear you very much."

When everything else failed, I began to mimic my brothers. "Out, you bold thing, out," I'd say, seizing our pet by the scruff of her neck and depositing her in the sand. Then as Chick pounded past us, whacking his chest, I'd ask, "Where do you get all this steam? Good night!"

Bernarr McFadden style, he lived in his bathing shorts and concentrated on HEALTH. Dedicated to building the body-beautiful regardless, he hauled us out of bed at dawn. "Get up, lazybones. We're going for a swim. Then I'll fix some bacon and eggs, yum-yum."

"Must you?" I'd moan, dragging a pillow over my head.

He'd yank off the covers. "Come alive. Here's your bathing suit."

"Aye, aye. But don't think I like this punishment."

After our swim, he'd stand under the ice-cold shower howling some ditty about a farmer taking another load away. Oh dear, I'd wonder, why didn't I marry an older man or something?

He insisted that the kids and I take showers too. "It's a real pepper-upper."

"But you know I loathe this."

"Nonsense. Jump in, my jolly. See how fine it feels."

"Man the masthead. There she blows," I croaked as needles of ice hit my back. "Mercy. Why must we do this?"

"Hurry up. After breakfast let's take a long walk up the beach."

"Brrrrr."

Each evening when we returned sandy and waterlogged to the cottage, we'd find mementos from visitors. "Sorry nobody was here. But we had a nice look-around anyway. P.S. My, but it's charming!" Sometimes there'd be visiting cards from people who had known us at school. "Hi, Martha. Cheerio." "If you have a free minute, Anne, do ring me."

". . . twenty-nine, thirty," Chick said, thumbing through this collection dismally. "If this keeps up, we'll need a social secretary or a padlock."

"Aren't you going to get out of those wet trunks, honey?"

"Why should I? They feel good."

"Someone else might call here before supper."

"We can always run off and hit for the hills."

Since the weather stayed perfect, we postponed excursions to town and sight-seeing. "There'll be plenty of time for ginger ice cream," we promised the kids, "and for the Whaling Museum and the rest. Let's enjoy this sunshine while we can."

Once we were on the beach with our baskets of lunch, Chick and I became utterly blissful. Sprawled side by side on the sand, we'd squint at our little ones occasionally. Or manage an answer with enormous effort. "Yes. No. Maybe. . . . Er . . . I guess so."

The sleepier we became, the more Jill and Charlie seemed to demand attention. Harking back to my childhood they'd ask, "Did your dad teach you all to swim before you learned to walk? Were you really the landlubber in your family?"

"Except for the Australian crawl, I got nowhere," I'd say, sighing.

"Will you teach me the crawl now?"

"Pretty soon . . . if you let me rest here a while."

After I had repeated my recollections of a blackfish invasion in 1918, they kept pleading for more. "Wake up, Mom. Go on. Be a sport."

Then when I resorted to snoring tactics, Jill said to Charlie, "Wouldn't it be fun if the fishermen chased a pack of them up here on the beach again? We could eat whale steak and everything."

"Ugh," he hollered delightedly. "I bet they taste nasty."

"They don't either; do they, Mom?"

I kept snoring.

"If we leave bread bait around, probably they'll come whistling and spouting. Then we can get out some big knives and whack them dead."

Another subject which enchanted the children was the game of Beaver popular in the "twenties." I had told them that it began in England and that we kids often played it together. "When we saw a man with a beard we'd shout 'Beaver.' Depending on the length of his whiskers you'd get one point or five, if you spotted him first."

"What if he had them right down to his toes?" Jill asked.

"He'd count ten, I suppose."

Since not even sideburns could be discovered on 1946-vintage bathers, Jill devised the game of Whale as solace. Stout passers-by in dark clothes would count one, those in white, five. Man-mountains, regardless of sex, color or creed, would be ten. Whoever first spotted his prize could claim him with the words "Whale Ahoy."

Once she had explained the rules, a battle royal began. "Whale Ahoy. . . . I said it first. . . . You didn't either. . . . I did so."

"What are they squalling about, Ern?"

"I'm too happy to care."

"Me too."

"She's fat, but not enough for five."

"Look again, you jerk. Isn't she a whopper?"

"I suppose we ought to stop this nonsense," Chick said. "But I can't move."

"Whale Ahoy one. . . . Whale Ahoy five. I saw him years before you!"

"Let's ignore them, Chick. Kids have to play. And this is harmless." I wriggled deeper into the sand. "It's heavenly here, isn't it?"

At the windup of our vacation rain came at last. Bundled into our slickers, the four of us boarded an excursion bus and settled back to enjoy the fun. Though we visited Sankaty Head Light and ate ginger ice cream in Siasconset, a neighboring village, the children were most impressed by our pause in front of The Shoe. "A family named Gilbreth raised a dozen youngsters here. Look sharp now and you may see some of them housekeeping here still. Those lighthouses used to be old channel markers, but they're used for sleeping quarters now."

"If the weather was better," Chick whispered, "I'd

have a look around and leave my card. 'P.S. The place is charming.' "

" 'If you have a free minute, Anne,' " I said, " 'do call me.' "

For every reason we postponed packing until the next and final afternoon. Since it was sunny and beautiful again by now, Chick and I couldn't help groaning. "Why did we bring all these clothes here, for goodness' sakes? We haven't used half of them."

Meanwhile the children were out in the front yard, greeting and turning away strangers. "Mother and Daddy are busy; so if you don't mind . . ."

Occasionally we'd hear them howling "Whale Ahoy" and scrapping over their scores. "Don't try to explain their rules to me," Chick said after asking a question or two. "The less I know about this nonsense the better."

"You're so right," I agreed, thumping some shoes into a suitcase.

Later, as wc dragged a duffelbag through the living room, Charlie shouted like a fog horn, "Whale Ahoy ten. Yikes, what a whopper."

"I said it too," Jill insisted. "But you didn't hear me."

"You did not, you liar. She's my whale and I got her before you even looked."

"She's mine. And you know it."

"Not so loud, children," I called over my shoulder. "And stop those horrid names."

As they continued to howl at each other, we heard a knock on the door. "Excuse me, young man," a huge woman in white marched in and addressed herself to Chick. "I knew I'd find some of you Gilbreths here. You're Bill, of course, aren't you?"

Purple in the face, he managed to say, "How do you do." Then in the next breath, "Ernie. Oh, Ernie."

But our friend had already discovered me. "Why, Martha dear, you haven't changed a bit." Two plump hands squeezed mine warmly. "You don't remember me, do you?"

I can't remember anything but that passage from *Moby Dick*, I thought. "Lo! Close under our lee . . . a gigantic whale lay rolling like the capsized hull of a frigate."

The children charged in and joined us now. "Listen, Dad. Charlie's being awful. . . . I am not, Daddy; I am not."

"Hush, will you?"

"No wonder you didn't know me, Martha," our visitor continued, ignoring the disturbance. "And I bet brother Bill here couldn't place me either." She smiled at Chick roguishly. "But your remarkable mother never forgets a face."

I won't forget this one either, I thought. In fact, it

will haunt me the rest of my life. Who is this woman? Why is she here?

"Time flies, doesn't it, Bill? Only yesterday, it seems, your father was bringing the crowd of you here. But you've grown inches since then."

Straightening himself instinctively, Chick banged his head on a beam.

"My husband keeps doing that," I said. "I'm Ernestine, not Martha, and . . ."

"I bet that hurt, didn't it, Bill?"

"Yes. But I'm not Bill. . . . I'm . . ."

"A little ice might relieve the pain, Martha. Why don't you run and get some?"

"It's nothing, Ernie. Please don't bother."

We're just not clicking here today, I thought. This is getting sillier and sillier. Is she hard of hearing or doesn't she listen?

"Now, Martha, these two little ones are Jane and Bob, aren't they?"

"No. Jill and Charles are Careys."

"At this rate, they won't be babies much longer. They were playing the sweetest sailing game as I came up the road. . . . Jane, you're the spit and image of Mother, aren't you?"

"I'm Jill," she said. "And this is Charlie."

"Is Mother here with you now, Bob? And have you learned to swim nicely yet?"

"Sure," he giggled. "Sure."

"Of course Mother's here," Jill said, edging toward me. "You are, aren't you, Mom?"

"I was," I said. "But now I'm not positive."

"Janey dear, will you tell Mother I've come to see her?"

Jill stared incredulously.

"But if she's napping, we won't interrupt her. Will we? "

"Oh no," Jill said, licking her lips.

Our visitor took my arm in hers. "She and I met only once, Martha. But that visit years ago was so pleasant."

"I wish Mother were here . . . but she isn't."

"She was so gracious when I introduced myself and asked to see the cottage. Not everyone would be so hospitable, you know."

"Mother Gilbreth is in Europe," Chick shouted.

"Run and call her if you insist, Bill. But don't feel you have to hurry."

"Before you go," I said a few minutes later, "would you like to leave a note and your name?"

"Beautiful island," she sighed. "There's no place like Nantucket, is there? It's a world apart." Smiling mistily, she wrung Chick's hand. "Watch those beams now, Bill."

"I will," he promised.

"Whale Ahoy ten," Charlie repeated to Jill, as our friend swam off into the distance. "And I saw her first."

"You didn't either."

"Well, brother-boy," I said to Chick, "now it's happened. Who am I?"

"Don't you know, Martha dear?"

"Guess you're right, Bill."

"I tell you what, Charlie," Jill said. "Let's split her in half and each take five points. O.K.?"

"All right, Jane. I mean Jill."

Leaving Nantucket was always sad; and especially so now. For there were no Gilbreths here to bid us good-by.

Yet we stood in a traditional cluster at the stern of the steamer, examining the wharf as we steamed away from it, the rocks at Brant Point, the dune in front of The Shoe. "It was a fine vacation," Chick said, breaking the silence. "But next time, Ern, let's be with your family; the more the merrier."

"Are all of you sure you want a next time here?"

"Of course. Don't you?" They looked thunderstruck.

" 'Beautiful island,' " I said. " 'It's a world apart.' "

"Come on, Mom. Stop teasing us. What do you say?"

"Whale Ahoy."

CHAPTER 16

Those in Favor Say Aye

DIFFERENCES add delight, maybe. But marriage would have been less of a dance for Chick and me if our childhood years had been more alike.

Chick was the older of two sons raised under conventional New England methods. His father was the Provider, master of all economic matters; his mother's domain was her home and little ones.

The youngsters didn't share in the handling of family problems. This was an era when small fry were supposed to be seen rather than heard. Dad and Mother Carey piloted their ships without dependence on the crew.

When Chick came to New York soon after high-school graduation, warm associations came with him. When he married several years later, he continued to recall his mother's domestic and artistic gifts. "There was nothing she couldn't do and do well," he'd say. "And no dad could have been a better guy than mine."

I had grown up with industrial-engineer parents. Since they believed that all phases of life are closely related, we practiced time-and-motion saving in our home. Before and after Daddy's death, we twelve kids shared fully in work, responsibilities and majority rule.

Though the Gilbreth way was a source of merriment to our friends sometimes, we knew that it made sense. Especially when we found it helpful in college and afterwards.

When the products of these two different American upbringings exchanged marriage vows, it was indeed for "better or worse." But the really big adjustments came after we had moved to Manhasset.

Turning to his boyhood for guidance, Chick became increasingly stern with the children. "March now, miss," he'd tell Jill. "I'm making the decisions for this family."

"Don't discourage them from asking why," I said one night.

"Suppose you listen to me, Ernie . . ." He ended with a eulogy of his earliest memories. "Sure, maybe Dad was strict. But we learned to toe the mark and follow instructions."

"That's important. But today we want Jill and Charlie to weigh reasons and think for themselves."

"Modern kids are too fresh. I won't let ours ride cowboy. Understand?"

Since there was no meeting of minds here, I decided to demonstrate the Gilbreth methods bit by bit. If I was lucky, action might speak louder than words.

We started simply with a family bulletin board in the kitchen. Next we fashioned a group calendar correlating all our social engagements: "Jill, play in backyard today with Susy. Charlie, shop groceries and shoes with Mother."

Then, having discussed the Gilbreth chart system, we set up one for the children, listing their jobs: toothbrushing, dumping wastebaskets, making beds. Chick became interested in spite of himself. "If this brain wave works, Ern, you deserve a hug and a blue ribbon."

"Watch. It can't miss."

Soon I was busily eating crow. At the end of the first week, when the kids collected less than half of their allowances, they screamed their heads off. "No fair. This is a gyp."

"Having a little trouble, honey?" Chick gloated.

We struggled for another month and got nowhere. "They say in school," Jill insisted, "that we should get an allowance without penalties. Grandear Gilbreth says so too."

When we found that our penniless ones had rifled the dime store, I was forced to agree. So we scrapped the chart system.

"Times change," Chick chuckled, quoting one of my mother's favorite expressions, "and we must change with the times."

Next, following my dad's methods again religiously, I

taught Jill touch typewriting. Within a week she was a whiz-bang, doing her school assignments in half the usual time. Several days later, though, she returned home in tears. "My teacher says I type better than I write. So now I have to do my papers by hand."

Since her skill fired interest in the neighborhood, several of Jill's friends wished to learn typewriting too. One of them succeeded in breaking all Gilbreth-Carey records for accuracy. "Next I'd like to learn the Morse code," he said, "if you'd like to teach it to me."

Repeating history again, we tried three-level dusting with Charlie doing the table legs, Jill the flat surfaces, me the upper ledges. While the children dawdled, I fumed. We did the dishes while they fought and pinched and howled. And Chick kept asking, "Why don't you give up, Ern? Can't you see you're licked?"

Belatedly, I realized that we had neglected to form a Family Council, giving the kids the thrill of participation. How stupid can you be, you dumb Dora? I asked myself. Without *this,* of course we're sunk.

The following Sunday we held our first meeting, electing Chick Council Chairman, and Jill Secretary. He had agreed to this after protesting vehemently. "In a large family I see why you needed officers and rules. But with just four of us here, it seems crazy. We're sure to vote two against two."

"Let's try it anyway," the children and I insisted.

Though Jill and Charlie were charmed by parliamentary procedure, Chick disliked it. "What? I'm supposed to pound the table and make a monkey of myself?"

"But Dad, in school we always do this. Come on. Be a sport."

Our suggestion that each speaker rise in turn, enunciating clearly, embarrassed him. "Jill, do you wish to say something?" he'd ask, flushing.

"Yes, Dad." She'd pop up like a jack-in-the-box. "We kids need a later bedtime."

"No siree, miss. Over my dead body."

Charlie would do his patter next. "Dad, let's get a pet."

"No siree, young man."

While we were learning the rudiments of home democracy, together, I kept thinking: This is hard work. It's more ticklish than playing with dynamite. How come it takes so much patience and tact?

Sometimes one or both children would rush off from our meetings in tears. Or Chick would slam down his gavel and quit his chairmanship. Or I'd tear my hair and shout, "What's the matter with all of us? Can't we talk without bellowing and fighting with each other?"

As our meetings improved, Jill and Charlie became enthusiastic. When they had succeeded in getting a later bedtime, bigger allowances, a goldfish and a new phonograph, they were less allergic to sharing in family responsibilities and work.

Several years later our budgeting committee authorized the purchase of a television set and an automobile. With Charlie stating the clincher for TV. "This way, Mom, you'll know what programs we watch. And we'll be home more."

After the committee had recommended a Ford convertible complete with radio and heater, the four of us trekked to the showroom. Two cars were available for immediate delivery: one gray, one red. We stood examining them, confounded by their beauty.

"Gee, Dad, look. Isn't that red job a honey?"

Chick and I had been looking . . . but in opposite directions.

"Isn't the gray nice?" I murmured.

He stood like a small boy, enchanted by a Christmas bicycle.

Sizing up the situation, Jill jumped into action. "Those in favor of red say Aye."

Three voices rose in a shout.

"Gray?"

"Red it is," I groaned.

When Chick had signed some papers and a check, he leaped into the driver's seat. "This is a moment to remember, Ern, eh?"

I stood there sulking.

He blew the horn a couple of times, beaming with satisfaction. "Jill was on the beam, wasn't she? I like to see kids thinking on their feet."

I still wasn't ready to speak.

He pushed the radio button and a soprano voice spilled out over us. "Smile, durn you, smile."

The devil I will, I thought.

"That council idea's good, Ernie. It's beginning to make real sense." He blew the horn again. "Jump in, honey. We'll go for a ride."

"I've been on one already," I grumped. "But if you and the kids insist . . ."

"Is everyone aboard?" he hollered as I closed the door behind me. "O.K., folks. Full steam ahead."

CHAPTER 17

Lady, Get Your License

SOME are born with automobiles, some achieve automobiles and some have automobiles thrust upon them.

Though we Careys achieved our car, my learning to drive was at Chick's insistence. "What's holding you back, for goodness' sakes? Any two-year-old knows how to steer."

Dipping into savings, we had bought a convertible after Jill had been in a bicycle accident. "It's good she knocked out her tooth that day," Charlie has said ever since, "else we'd be walking our legs off still."

If there was anything good about Jill's spill from a neighboring child's handle bars, I can't recall it. Instead there was a phone call and a woman's tense voice. "Your little girl needs to see a doctor immediately. She's in considerable pain." Then, "No, Mrs. Carey. Please don't call a taxi. My car's right here in the driveway. We'll pick you up as we come by."

A couple of weeks later when the replanted tooth took root, our dental surgeon clapped his hands. "This is amazing, really. The child's going to be good as new. It was fortunate you got here so promptly."

All this, as Charlie insists, may have pushed us into a purchase that we wouldn't have made otherwise. In any case, once we voted Aye, Chick was like a schoolboy. "Since we're buying a car, folks, let's get a sporty model."

No one could have been more triumphant than he was with his new toy. He kept polishing its gorgeous body and glass. He blew its horn for sheer pleasure. He insisted that we keep taking family excursions. "How about it? Want to see a bit of the country?"

Once he was behind the wheel, he was ready to fight every car on the road. "Get off my back, you blankety-blank buzzard," he'd shout while I squirmed. "Where did you get your license . . . from Sears Roebuck?"

There were other reasons why I didn't share his pleasure. While the kids romped in the back seat, Winnie-the-Pooh would wind herself around my neck. Meantime, incessant comments about women drivers came again and again. "Where does that stupid daughter-of-misery think she's going today?"

"Please, Chick. Watch your tongue."

"Why?"

"You know that women are involved in fewer accidents than men. In a crisis, they use consistently better judgment."

"Ho. Who says so?"

"An article I read recently."

"The writer needs a new head then."

Soon Charlie was copying him. "What else can you expect from a woman? Eh, Dad?"

When I presented statistics defending the "gentler sex," Chick hooted. "Those figures are cranked up . . . and you know it." In the next breath he'd urge me to get a learner's permit and a teacher immediately. "If the kids need a doctor again, you must be ready to jump."

This was true enough. But still I kept stalling.

"You're a grown woman, Ernie. Be brave. Live in the present; forget the past."

It was a grievance between us that my fears were partly Chick's fault. In the Linville days, after Jill's birth, I had achieved a license and let it lapse. The decision to drive no more *ever* had come after a Sunday outing with me at the wheel.

"Good God," Chick had screamed as I turned corners or stepped on the gas pedal. "Do you want to kill us both? Brake her. *Brake* her. Here. Let me drive. Move over."

Afterwards I wouldn't speak to him. (I was plenty confused by his thinking too. Break our precious car? Why, for goodness' sakes?)

"I happen to value my neck a little," he said bitterly. "Even if you don't."

But my phobias had begun years before our marriage.

Experience in two collisions with collegemates had convinced me that shoe leather is safer than wheels.

"Those nightmares are behind you," Chick said when I confessed them.

Unfortunately, they weren't, though.

With a fluttering heart, I began one of the biggest ordeals of my life. After passing eye, ear and literacy tests, I got my learner's permit. Then I contacted Mr. Lark, a professional instructor. "You'll learn to drive or else," he said as we made our first appointment.

My man appeared the next day in a sky-blue outfit exactly matching his jeep. "We'll use your car in case we crack up," he said blithely. "Get behind the wheel, missus; turn on the ignition." Settling himself beside me, he measured the distance to the door.

After getting reacquainted with the clutch, brake and gas pedal, I steered us down the driveway to the street. Soon we were roaring through traffic. "In five minutes I'll know whether you'll be a menace on the road," Mr. Lark promised. "Skinny-merincks bust out of control the worst sometimes."

I was working too hard to speak.

As we passed a group of dogs, he warned, "Don't crash a car because of animals obstructing the way. Blow. Slow down. Leave them mind theirselves."

When we had spun off the highway, he began to quiz me. "What does a stop sign look like, missus?"

"It's octagonal."

"No. Eight-sided. What does it tell you to do?"

"To stop."

"No, that won't pass the inspector. Say it like the book: 'Bring your car to a full stop.' . . . What does a square sign mean?"

I didn't know.

" 'A square sign means caution. Be prepared to meet a possible operating hazard such as a crossroad.' "

"Or another driver?"

"Read the book."

"What does a diamond sign mean? Say it with me now. 'A diamond sign means reduce speed for permanent physical hazards.' What is a hazard?"

"Me, I guess."

"It isn't either. Read the book."

It was becoming increasingly clear that two unique characters had found each other. When I confessed my nervousness to Mr. Lark, he slapped my wrist. "Look, dear. Are you paying me to be sorry or to teach you today?"

When we returned home, he confided a little secret. "You couldn't head through the windshield today, even if you tried. See? . . . I kept my foot under the gas pedal."

Having steeled myself to a series of lessons, I was ready to take the next one immediately. But Mr. Lark had other plans. "I'm going to lay abed and take it easy for the next two weeks. Practice driving with your husband now."

"No. Not on your life," Chick said when I suggested that we take evening twosomes together. "I'd rather be shot."

"Please, honey."

"What became of that bohunkus you picked? How come, after one lesson, he hits for the hills?"

"He's very very tired."

"I believe it."

"But he says I did well this morning."

"Maybe he didn't want to hurt your feelings."

When everything went wrong during our practice sessions, Chick blamed Mr. Lark's teaching. "Is this how he told you to shift, for Heaven's sake? Don't you ever signal? Stop riding the clutch. Murder."

One late afternoon, with Charlie an additional passenger, I stalled halfway up a hill. Cussing under his breath, Chick dived for the brake with one hand and grabbed his son with the other. "No wonder Lark quit," he mumbled as we got under way again.

"I hear husbands shouldn't try to teach their wives," Jill said at supper. "Are you patient always, Daddy?"

Glaring, he refused to answer.

During our second lesson, Mr. Lark warned about road intersections. "Don't be so nosy, missus. While you're snooping in there, someone's liable to bang your rear end good. Keep your eye on what's ahead."

After this, whenever I was too nosy, he slapped my wrist twice.

Later, as I finished the dozenth U turn, he said, "A little sweat never hurt nobody; the fatties especially."

If I swerved to avoid squirrels or crows, my teacher was furious. "Leave them fur and feathers lay. Your life might mean more, remember."

By our third lesson we were buddies. Because of the torrid weather Mr. Lark had donned a mesh shirt, suspenders and an ancient straw hat. I observed that he prided himself on being a gentleman, a psychologist and an expert with women. Yet his squint, gold teeth and down-East twang suggested a wider variety of gifts.

Today, as usual, we began with the sign quiz game: eight-sided, square and diamond-shaped. "I see you done your homework good, missus," he said as we finished. "If you pass *my* test, them inspectors will be chicken feed."

I had learned that several years before he had helped to compile the State Driving Manual: "But it took too much out of me."

When I had U-turned endlessly again, Mr. Lark grew chatty. An increasing number of doctors, he said, were prescribing driving lessons for mental patients. "They send them to me instead of to a sanitarium. . . . Now and again one of us blows off, of course. But nobody keeps a grudge to the other fellow long."

He said that he had marked me from the beginning as being "calm on top and high-stringed underneath. . . . But I'm beating it out of you by degrees."

His tales about his pupils seemed to mark many of them as "high-stringed" too. There was the overshy matron who couldn't bear to drive with her knees held apart. She wouldn't wear slacks either, until, at Mr. Lark's insistence, her husband suggested them. "She got her license, missus; and she's been wearing them slacks ever since. I saw her downtown yesterday in a red pair, big as a fire truck."

There was the woman who smacked the curb whenever she tried to park. Mr. Lark decided she needed to flunk her test before learning to heed his instruction. But Mrs. Lark disagreed. " 'What does the lady look like?' says wifey. So I told her she was got up pretty as a doll every lesson, with hats fit for a picture show.

"And you know what, missus? The next day, when Doll Baby kept hitting the curbs again, I followed wifey's orders. 'No wonder you can't drive when you wear such crazy hats,' I says. 'Blind as a bat, aren't you?' Then I made her park for fair.

"She done a perfect job, too. . . . 'My, Mr. Lark,' she

says, 'how you got around me. After those insults, I *had* to succeed.' "

Another interesting pupil was the French woman who drove "like buzzards was on her tail. . . . She wore next to nothing, missus, except right *here* and *here.* I tried to make Madame see that the inspectors would object and flunk her pronto. 'Wear something loose and comfortable tomorrow,' I'd hint. . . . But do you think she'd listen?

"Darned if next day that woman didn't take her test in the same postage-stamp outfit. So tight, mind you, she couldn't sneeze. After the boys gave the big NO treatment, she got wise and learned to dress modest. But those Frenchies don't have sensitivities like you and I."

Still another pupil had been divorced by her husband after she had wrecked his new Cadillac. "When she stripped the gears, their first lesson together, he lost patience. Mind you, I'm not saying this caused the divorce. But it was a contributing cause, she told me."

During our next lesson, Mr. Lark concentrated on building Ego and Bravery. We were on an express highway, surrounded by trucks, at the time. "Never be scared, missus. As a woman and a fine one, remember you was never terrorized in your life."

Stepping on the gas, I absorbed every word.

"You've grown matured and you have two lovely children. You went through labor pains, didn't you? An experience your husband never had . . . nor me neither."

Egad, I thought.

"Green light ahead now," he shouted. "Step on her, for God's sake, missus. Move. Before someone piles up on your rear."

"I had an experience you never had in your life," I told Chick that night.

"What?"

"Labor pains and two lovely children. Mr. Lark says so."

"If that's all you learned from that featherhead today, we've wasted three dollars."

"Don't insult the man I love."

In spite of our affection, my teacher and I were at odds during the last instruction period. As I made one fumble after another, he kept shouting and slapping my wrist. "Is this how I learned you, missus? Fie, fie and for shame."

He found my signals too short. He groaned as I turned or parked. He burst with rage as I proceeded through traffic on an orange light. "So land in jail, you blundering female."

The more he scolded, the more panicky I became. Finally I drew over to the curb and stopped. "I can't go on. I can't."

He drew a long, painful breath. "Maybe I'm twitchy with your test coming up tomorrow. But you aren't doing like I told you."

I bowed my head.

"You're wasting your husband's money and gas too. So give up now, missus. Admit you're yellow." After lighting a cigarette, he puffed it wildly.

"You confuse me," I cried.

"Holy saints, what do you think you do to me?"

When we were calm again, we apologized profusely. On the way home, Mr. Lark continued to stress my need to relax at the wheel. "Then you'll breeze through them inspectors like a dose of salts."

I did, too . . . and received my license promptly. And why not? My man had been a second Mr. Lark, so his test seemed easy. In addition, I had remembered to be hatless, to wear loose slacks and to recite the Driving Manual with reverence.

It had been delightful; easier than labor pains and childbirth.

Yet once the State of New York had given its blessing, Chick began to use the car increasingly. "Special customers will be in town today, Ernie. So if you don't mind . . ."

He'd buzz off while I stood wondering why I had ever struggled with driving lessons.

During week ends and whenever we went on family

rides, he'd insist on taking the wheel. "Sorry, dear. But this way it's safer."

I accepted the situation stoically.

"Don't you ever drive?" friends ask sometimes.

"Walking is simpler," I say.

CHAPTER 18

Permanent-Wave Party

I HAVE never liked the New England expression, "Save at the spigot and spend at the bung." If, as Chick says, it is custom-made for us Careys, I like it all the less.

Regardless, during the years when we have been investing in a house, a car, a washing machine and the rest, I have continued to save string, wrapping paper, old spools and jars. Also diaries, clippings, letters, telegrams and sentimental mementos dating back to Moses. Meanwhile Chick keeps hoarding hotel soap, shirt cardboard, matchboxes and fodder for his compost heap.

As a family, we like to think that we are thrifty. But when we spend we take a long breath and jump.

In some cases, my economies give no more pleasure than a bed of spikes. I continue to mend cavernous holes in socks and dungarees. (Until Chick had to hot-foot home from business one day, I made a point of replacing zippers.) I lengthen sleeves, alter curtains, home dry-clean, use up leftovers in casseroles, try my hand at beauty care and other frustrations. And a dollar saved is a dollar gained, temporarily at least.

Luckily, I have acquired some skill with a comb, scissors, curling pins and wave lotion. But of all devil gadgets, these require the most deadly patience.

Snipping at the children's blond crops in the past, I have recalled Kipling's lines stoically:

> If you can keep your head when all about you
> Are losing theirs and blaming it on you,
> If you can trust yourself when all men doubt you,
> But make allowance for their doubting too . . .

"You were in mischief again, weren't you?" neighbors would ask Charlie after our shearing sessions. "Look at that big bare spot there."

Finally, when he was four, he blubbered to Chick, "Make Mommy stop it. Take me where you go, Dad."

Since one of Chick's economies is minimum tonsorial care, the expense has been slight. When the Messrs. Carey visit their emporium, they look like twin Samsons, before and after.

Jill's era of cooperation ended the day I sliced her ear. Though she let me trim bangs occasionally after this, both of us kept trembling. Finally we called it quits.

Once she had learned to coiffure herself expertly, she took me in hand too. Aside from the time involved (one hour for a shampoo, two for a set), results have been stupendous. To those blessed with clever fingers and a sense of perfection, hairdressing may come naturally.

She is chagrined, of course, not to have been born with

a cascade of curls. But with determination and the help of modern science, she has achieved them.

Though permanent waves on children have seemed a sort of stigma to me always, I gave Jill her first when she was seven. "It's *my* life, you know," she had insisted.

Since I mislaid the directions when we were halfway through, we were forced to depend on hunch. Afterwards there was no sign of a tendril. Undaunted we tried again the following Saturday. For good measure this time, we added an extra hour of processing. The result, of course, was steel wool. "Gee, Mom. Did you *try* to make me hideous?"

Eventually, after spending an entire day in the bathroom, she achieved a ravishing transformation. From this point on, she continued to look, walk and pose like a Hollywood starlet.

Watching her, I felt my eyes misting sometimes. Our dear little girl, getting to be a young lady so soon?

"She's getting vain," Chick protested. "Why do you encourage this razzle-dazzle?"

"I'm not encouraging it."

"Maybe you think you're not."

Jill kept experimenting with new dramatic effects: the brushed innocent type, the flutter bug, page boy, horsetail and windstorm. She pirouetted before the mirror until I warned, "Handsome is as handsome does."

"Mother, if you say that again I'll scream."

"You're wasting too much time, honey."

"But think what a hairdresser would cost."

This reminder always hit home.

As time went on, she became more and more concerned with my appearance. "If you'd spend more time on yourself, you could be prettier than Betty's mother. . . . Why don't you brush your hair a hundred strokes a day? . . . Why don't you?"

Seeking to build me into the schoolgirl's dream of yesterday's bride, she offered to give me a permanent wave. "You need one, don't you? And I'd love to fix you."

Perhaps I should have pondered that word "fix." But I didn't.

When Chick and Charlie heard us making plans for the next Saturday, they hurriedly bought tickets to a ball game. "That goo you use makes us sick," they said, holding their noses.

It will be more serene without them here, I thought. They'll have fun and we girls will have a picnic together.

Once our men had kissed us good-by, Jill and I got busy. While I stripped and ducked my head into the basin, she set up her equipment. "What will it be today, modomme? . . . Zee henna rinse or ze beeeautiful platinum?" Grinding my nose into the porcelain, she began to shampoo.

I made a bubble-blowing sort of noise from below.

"You know, Mom, in school we keep a cage of hamsters in our room. They keep mating almost every minute. Don't you guess there'll be babies pretty soon?"

" I can't hear you too well, honey," I said coming up for air.

"You're dripping. Get down there. When the babies come . . . how will it be *exactly?*"

Before I could answer she pushed me back into Davy's locker again. "Stay there and don't move, modomme." Yo ho ho and a bottle of rum, I thought, gulping.

The doorbell rang insistently.

"Darn it. Stay where you are. I'll be back in a flash." After a last push at my head, she dashed downstairs.

Crouching, waterlogged and blinded, I waited for five minutes. Would my helper ever return?

"Hey, Mom." Her voice came at last. "We've been talking a little. The Girl Scouts are here selling cookies. How many shall we take?"

"Two boxes."

"Vanilla or chocolate?"

"One of each."

An hour later when we reached the wave-lotion stage, over a dozen youngsters had come in sequence. Each time the doorbell rang, Jill would fly off toward it. "Will the baby hamsters be hungry the very first minute?" she'd call over her shoulder. "Don't forget to tell me when I come back."

Next came chatter and giggles from below. "Say, that new bracelet looks pretty, doesn't it? Where were you yesterday? We had the most super time." Then when I was dancing with annoyance, "How many boxes this time, Mom?"

"One of each."

"Still?"

"Still."

Other callers seemed determined to interrupt us too: the oilman, the water-meter inspector, a woman selling aprons and a boy soliciting magazine subscriptions.

While Jill took care of them, I stood in my underpants, dripping and forlorn. Would this idleness ever stop? Would I ever again return to civilization, dressed to the teeth?

After each trip to the door or telephone she'd examine my head monkey-style. Then she'd redo several curls.

"Must you keep going backwards, honey? Can't you take pity, please? We'll be here all night."

"No we won't," she'd carol as the bell rang again.

By late afternoon we reached the final rinse, with my spine at a breaking point. Having discarded her roles as professional hairdresser and little-one-searching-into-the-facts-of-life, Jill now became patient-mother-soothing-truculent-offspring. "Don't twist and turn so. That's a good girl."

Who's who in this dreary tea party, I wondered?

As I kept brooding over this switcheroo, Jill glanced at the clock and hollered, "Look, Mom. It's almost five and I'm due at choir practice. Oh murder."

"I couldn't care less," I said bitterly.

"But you'll need to drive me there. This minute."

I dug at my streaming eyes and hair. "What are you talking about, Jill Carey? I'm half drowned. Look at me."

"But you know Mr. Dean raises cain if we're late. Get on your clothes, quick. Hurry."

"Even Lady Godiva wasn't put on this spot," I moaned.

"But you've got to help me."

After wrenching on a shower cap, I dressed and jumped into the car. We drove for several blocks in silence. As we stopped for a red light a voice piped from nowhere, "Look at that funny lady. She's been swimming."

"Tee hee hee," Jill cackled. "I'm sorry, but tee hee hee."

When I returned to our driveway, two neighbors were waiting on the steps. "The water was delightful," I told them. "Do come in."

After I had signed checks for their charities, they combed and set my hair in pin curls. "It's a beautiful wave, Ern. . . . Which one did you use?"

"Ezy-Quik," I said. "Only it wasn't."

When our baseball contingent came home a half hour

later, I was buying two last boxes of cookies. "Well, Ernie," Chick said, examining my polliwog head and the stacks of vanilla and chocolate, "you went overboard today, didn't you?"

"Yes," I said.

CHAPTER 19

Turnabout Is Only Fair

UNTIL a few years ago, Chick and I held strongly different convictions about schoolteachers. Flinching at memories of his boyhood, he identified Mr. or Miss Grump with ruler-raps-across-his-wrist, "Horatius at the Bridge" elocutions ("which shouldn't happen to a dog") and a nasal, stuffed-shirt demeanor.

In contrast, I have always had the deepest love for this profession. The roots for this unquestionably stretch back through many generations of schoolteaching kin, including my New England Gilbreth grandmother. Entangled in them too are a former elementary-school teacher, another in high school and two others in college, who *never* compared me with my sister Anne and gave everlastingly of themselves.

"Why do you have this Allah-Allah attitude?" Chick has asked sometimes. "More and more you spend time at the kids' schools or go along on classroom jaunts. Can't you get enough of this ever?"

"It's like measles," I say. "Once you catch the germ, it *gets* you. From top to toe."

After batting this subject back and forth a bit, I usually remind him that Jill's or Charlie's teacher will be coming to dinner next week. "This way she can see and enjoy us as a family. And get insights."

"Ho. Unless you straighten up this house a little, she'll get a double eyeful."

"Who cares? This way it's homelike."

"Too damn homelike, if you ask me."

"Well, she's interested in people rather than things."

"Ho."

Though I had started two years of department-store buying in 1947, our pattern in Manhasset stayed unchanged. The offer of a job in New York City had come soon after we had located a fine sleep-in housekeeper, a coincidence too tempting to resist. And we had agreed that with Charlie in nursery school now, "Mother might as well keep busy."

Friday night continued to be teacher-visiting night, since Maggie had her "day off" then and the children could help serve supper. Once we had welcomed Miss Smith or Miss Jones, Jill or Charlie would take her upstairs. "Maybe you'd like to see my room . . . and my books and radio . . ."

From below, Chick and I would catch bits of conversation. "I keep Jeanne Crain's picture by my bed, because she's so beautiful. This is my Sunday School certificate, my woolly animals and my favorite miniatures." After a pause we'd hear Charlie pipe, "Yup, Brooklyn's my favorite team lately . . . Jackie Robinson. I keep batting averages near my desk . . . and Daddy helps me."

Inevitably we winced as the discussion grew increasingly confidential. "This bureau is a pigpen usually; but since you were coming, we house-cleaned. Mother's room's a sight sometimes; so she keeps the door closed. Daddy's the neat type of course. . . until it's painful."

"Good God," Chick said in an undertone, "next they'll be describing me in my B.V.D.'s. Haven't we any privacy?"

"What does it matter? Observing a class in session always opens my eyes. Turnabout is only fair."

"Nonsense. I managed to graduate without all this hocus-pocus. I'm beginning to feel like a Peter Arno cartoon, drat it."

"Sssh," I'd warn as his voice reached the roof tops. "Must you broadcast it?"

"We have Family Council meetings," Charlie announced on another occasion. "But Daddy likes to boss too much. And Mother gets mad."

"I see you have endless hobbies here," Miss Dwyer, one of our favorite teachers, said on her first visit. "Let's see. Each of you owns his own typewriter . . . Yes? And countless books and collections. Charlie, why didn't you tell me you love stamps? I'll bring some South American ones to school tomorrow."

"Gee. Thanks."

"I guess no one has much time for television."

"Daddy does . . . more than the rest of us. He loves sports."

"I like lessons about cooking the best," Jill said. "My cookies taste better than Mother's."

"But my spaghetti is best in the family," Charlie crowed, "the thin kind especially. I make it Sunday nights sometimes."

"When he eats it I sing a song about worms crawling in and out. It drives him screamy-daffy." They rejoined us now.

"That's enough," Chick said severely. "You kids go light somewhere else, will you?"

"I'm enjoying them," Miss Dwyer told him. "Hospitality like this makes me feel at home. My, isn't this a lovely living room! How you must look forward to being here together." Then as Winnie scrambled up into her lap, "And you too, doggie. Yes?"

Since Dora Dwyer was young and blonde and winsome, Chick began to change some of his ideas on schoolmarms. "If Jill is half as intelligent and charming and sweet some day," he'd say after one of her visits, "I'll believe we succeeded as parents. But how did a glamour girl like that decide to take up *education?* Why didn't she choose something more exciting?"

I'd fight back the impulse to glare at him.

"Years ago I could have learned under a beauteous creature like that one. Youngsters today certainly are lucky. Boy oh boy."

One winter evening when Miss Dwyer came for dinner, we had a completely unexpected experience, all because of her new pocketbook. "I'm using it for the very first time," she told us, depositing it near a steaming radiator. "My brother brought this from Europe. Until now, it's seemed too lovely to sport around with."

After dinner, when we returned to the living room, something new had taken over there: a smell strong and poignant as a stable. "Peuw," Charlie said, grabbing his nose. "Wow."

Having delivered a hideous retching noise, Jill joined the nose club too.

"Golly," Charlie wheezed. "Did some horses come by here? Jeez."

"Children never bottle up anything, do they?" our guest asked gaily.

Chick fought back a smile.

Charlie had begun to scramble around the rug on his hands and knees, sniffing like a hound dog. "It gets worse here," he said, approaching the radiator. "To tell you the truth, it's awful."

"Winnie, did you forget yourself?" Jill asked loudly.

"Ahem," Chick said, frowning at her. "Ahem. Ahem. Ahem."

"Well, what else could it be, Dad?"

"Maybe a neighbor put some strong fertilizer on his lawn," I said hopefully. "My, it's powerful, isn't it? . . . Kerchoo!"

"Very," Dora Dwyer said, sneezing again and again. "Oh dear. Where's my handkerchief . . . in my handbag?" When she had hurried across the room, plucked her handkerchief out and applied it to her nose, she gasped, "I'm the guilty one. That leather is simply unspeakable. Ugh. Please forgive me."

"O.K., we will," Jill said in her most gracious manner. "But handsome is as handsome does. So I'd put that *lovely* stinker-*upper* in the garbage pail. Fast."

Of all our teacher friends, Frieda Zabrinsky was the most stimulating, filling a special place in everyone's heart. Firing and challenging her students' curiosity, she drew them into ever-widening experience. "Reading is fine, of course," she told them, "but we need to see and hear and feel things, if we're going to understand them. Don't we?"

Night after night now, Jill entertained us at dinner with "what I learned today." . . . "You know what? We sang Brahms' Lullaby and wrote our autobiographies and did a funny Polish dance. And next week we're taking another trip to New York City. You're chaperoning three girls and me, Mom. O.K.?"

"Fine," I'd say, pondering how to adjust to her plans. "I'll be there."

Once Frieda Zabrinsky and Chick had met at our house, they warmed toward each other. "It's wonderful to see our youngsters enjoying school," he told her. "They never have to learn nightmares now, do they, like 'Horatius at the Bridge'?"

Throwing back her shoulders and her head she recited several lines. "Don't I remember that horror, Mr. Carey? And what good did it do really?"

"It turned me against poetry forever . . . if you can call that balderdash poetry."

"Me too . . . for a while. There should have been a law against it."

"I think Ernie loves your New York excursions as much as Jill does," he said later. "She got a special bang out of the Museum of Natural History and that jaunt all of you made through her department store."

"You would too, if you'd come along."

He ducked.

"I'm serious. You know little things always impress youngsters so much more keenly than the big. For example, they never overlook a spray of tiny blossoms in the zebra display or a mouse hidden in a clump of grass."

His eyes began to shine.

"I try to be ready for questions. But of course I'll never know half what I should. There's such a vast amount to learn, isn't there?"

Leaning toward her he asked, "What did the kids like best in the museum . . . the parade of elephants?"

"No indeed. Year after year they go mad for the dried human heads in the Peruvian wing. But parents never understand their enthusiasm. Last time one of our mothers was almost sick."

He grinned. "I can see why she would be. Now how about that trip to Ernie's store? I heard you followed a piece of merchandise from receiving department to customer."

"We did. And oh my aching feet. How you stand the pace there, Mrs. Carey, I just don't know."

"Once you get used to it, you enjoy the pressure . . ."

Swallowing hastily, Jill said to her father, "Before we began that tour I told Mother, 'Don't be a buyer today or say anything embarrassing.' So she kept way behind us and everything was fine."

Then after nodding to Miss Zabrinsky, she added, "We liked the toy department and a fat lady losing her petticoat. But that duplicating machine upstairs somewhere really was perfect, because one of the boys knew how to work it and he got ink all over his nose. Honestly."

"Gad," Chick said. "In one breath you've jumped us

from toys and petticoats to ink. When will you learn to pause between sentences?"

"But Daddy, if you'd only listen . . ."

"Why was a duplicating machine so stupendous, Jill?"

She looked at him blankly. "How would I know?"

"One reason," I said, "was that our guide drew a blank when the kids asked what it was. But now she knows it's a rotary mimeograph model with a top cylinder and oscillating roller like the one in Frankie Davis's father's office. Incidentally, she told me afterwards that Jill and her classmates were the most observing visitors in years. . . . But if they come again, she'll quit."

"Don't blame her a bit," Chick said sympathetically.

"Come on, Daddy," Jill urged. "Please finish your dessert. Charlie and I are waiting to put on a show."

"She's so shy at school . . . and so different here," Miss Zabrinsky said when the children had run off to fetch some costumes. "Why? I wonder. Are we going wrong somewhere? How can we help her? How?"

No one was happier than Chick when Frieda announced her engagement several years later. "Why not bring that man of yours over to dinner?" he urged. "What's he got . . . sideburns and an English accent?"

"Richard is sort of tweedy and kind and awfully fond of children. In some ways, he's a great big bear."

"You mean he has hair all over his chest?" Jill asked, entranced. "Can't we ask him to let us see it, please?"

"He especially wants to meet you, dear. He's heard about your poetry and stories. He says you must have a very vivid imagination."

"That's the understatement of the year," Chick groaned.

"But Jill's so fortunate. Think of the pleasure this will give her over the years."

"When your best beau comes," Jill said very seriously, "we'll entertain him right. Charlie and I promise."

"Tell Richard he rates already," Chick said under his breath. "He may be in for more of a field day than he expects."

At last our big Friday-night get-together took place, with the children bubbling with excitement. Once we had shaken hands, I settled myself on the sofa with Richard while Chick exclaimed over Frieda's gifts: jelly and mixed pickles. "You made these yourself, you wonderful girl?"

"That's how she snared me," Richard said. "Invited me again and again to home-cooked meals with all the fixings. Completely broke my resistance to schoolmarms."

Throwing back his head suddenly, Chick thundered, "Young man, what does a ruler remind you of?"

"A rap on the wrist, sir. Hard."

"Did you ever have to write a sentence five hundred times?"

"*Did* I? Until my little old fingers were black and

blue. . . . As for the pages and pages of memorizing . . ."

"Absolute rot," Chick was bellowing still. "Shouldn't happen to a dog."

"You're speaking of the profession I love," Frieda said. "Where are those jars I brought? I'm going to take them right home."

"No you don't. I'm going to eat them tonight, down to the last lick, you Indian giver."

"Please, if I can interrupt a minute," Jill said to Richard, "Charlie and I want to see the hair on your chest. Is it there still?"

"I think so, honey. Let's open this shirt button and find out."

" 'We need to see and feel things,' " I said, teasing Frieda, " 'if we're going to understand them.' "

"Yikes," Jill hollered, staring incredulously. "Did you grow this all by yourself?"

Charlie too had placed his chin a breath away from this miracle. "When you get married and have babies will they wear little bearskins too?"

Glancing helplessly at his betrothed one, Richard rolled his eyes. "Who got me into this dandy hay ride? You?"

Soon we sat down to dinner, exclaiming over the children's place cards and elaborate Jack Horner Pie. "We'll pull strings and read each poem aloud," Jill said. "Then we'll open our gifts because this is a party."

"Hooray. Hooray," we chanted.

"Afterwards there'll be a show entitled *Times Are Hard All Over*. You'll see why, Daddy, especially."

An hour later we grownups settled ourselves in a row of chairs. "Pay attention now, folks," Jill ordered. "We're ready to start."

Act One opened with Charlie sleeping on the floor until Jill appeared in a sheet. "I am the Ghost of Schooldays Past," she told him. "Come with me, dear, and I'll open your eyes . . . because it shouldn't happen to a dog."

In the next scene, decked in a blouse and trailing skirt, she brandished a clothes pole. Charlie, naked except for his underdrawers, sat shivering at a desk. (Identifying himself with the situation, Chick began to chuckle.)

"Recite 'She Sells Sea Shells by the Seashore,' young man. Fast and perfectly. Do you hear me?"

"I can't say it," Charlie giggled, "and I *won't*."

"Then take this." She hit him hard across the seat. "And this. And this, you bad, bad boy."

Once he had limped off stage, screaming, she put on one of my hats. "Ladies and gentleman. . . . As you see, I have now become Mrs. Ernestine Carey. Though we are hearing my husband's story tonight, he wasn't the only one with troubles, years ago. No indeedy. If you don't believe me, suppose you listen." She began to do a Highland Fling and shout ecstatically, "Too bad you're not good in arithmetic, dearie; your sister was such a whiz. Too bad you're a dope at geography, dearie . . ."

"She did you proud, Ernie," Chick chortled during the next costume change. "And I'm glad you gave her that hat; I never liked it . . . much too extreme."

After the Ghost of Schooldays Present had made her announcement, Jill got into her mother getup again. Next Charlie strutted forward in what were supposed to be his father's business clothes.

"It was fun visiting the children's classrooms tonight," Jill said with forced gaiety. "Wasn't it, Chick?"

"Fun, hell. I've done my duty, Ernie, but I'm crippled for life . . ." As Charlie paused helplessly, Jill kept cueing him. "Those blasted chairs should be larger . . . or my great big fat bottom should be smaller. . . . Next time you'll have to drag me there. . . ."

"And did you see Jill's desk tonight, dear? Wasn't it orderly?"

"Haw. As usual it looked full of old garbage and mess."

"Why, Chick Carey, is that nice talk for a gentleman?"

"I'm no gentleman; I'm your husband. Haw. Haw. . . . Hey, who's this Miss Zabrinsky woman? Why doesn't she teach those kids something useful? My teacher kept drilling us again and again and again. Lots of lovely memory work too."

"Did you like it?"

"Sure. Good discipline. Fine. Fine."

"Honey, before I forget . . . I've asked Miss Zabrinsky to come to dinner next Friday. Aren't you happy?"

"Good night! Another teacher here again? . . . Beat me, bully me, starve me, but please not *that*."

"Curtain," Charlie yelped while Chick and I sat blushing and trying to smile. "We're really good, aren't we, folks?"

"Stupendous," Chick muttered, "like a blow in the stomach."

But Frieda and Richard had been laughing uproariously. Thank the Lord they understand and accept this, I thought. Otherwise it would be sheer, unadulterated torture. Golly.

Once the Ghost of Schooldays Future had given her patter, Charlie (in his father's smoking jacket and slippers) appeared in the last stages of senility. A moment later Jill arrived in a bridal outfit, carrying a baby.

"Oooops," Chick said, beginning to enjoy himself again. "She got her dates mixed, didn't she?"

"Daddy, I want you to meet your new little grandson, Charles the Third. . . . He's so brilliant we're sending him to school already."

"Humph. I hope he's housebroken and has some manners. Let's see that monkey-devil, eh?"

"Already he's learned his numbers wonderfully. Want to hear him?" She placed her child in his arms.

"Harumph. Not especially. But if you insist . . ."

A voice began to sing-song: "Two and two are four; eight and eight are sixteen . . ."

"Excellent, my boy. Excellent. Couldn't do better myself."

"He recites like anything too. Yesterday, in his bath, he did 'Hiawatha' . . . all the way through."

"Good. That will help some day when he starts out into the world."

"And Latin and French come so easily, it's terrific."

"That will help too. He'll thank you for it, believe me."

"But there's one great big disappointment, Daddy dear." Jill began to sob and tear her hair now. "He's simply a zero at sports."

"What did you say? Who wants a no-good like that? Get rid of him. Throw him out. We've been robbed. Murder."

"I'm sorry, oh I'm sorry," Jill kept wailing. "As a parent, I did my best."

"Curtain," Charlie shouted, kicking off his slippers. "You've *had* it, folks."

Yes, I thought. We certainly have . . . right between the eyes.

"Well, well, well," Chick said gamely, "they worked hard on that show. It hit the bull's-eye. Ow!"

"What was the title again?" I asked him. "*Times Are Hard All Over?* . . . Isn't that cute?"

"Oh my aching head," he said, rubbing his temples. "Ow."

"I'm itching for a song fest," Frieda said, sensing our discomfort. "Do you mind if I take a try at your piano? What shall we start with, Chick?"

"I wonder if you know one of my favorite songs?" Settling himself on the bench beside her, he began to croon it:

> What is it makes the grass so green?
> What makes the sky to blue?
> Some of these things you must surely knoooooow;
> Bobolink, answer me true.

As Frieda thumped out the first chords, Richard, the children and I gathered close, bellowing in harmony.

"We're fabulous," Jill said when we had sung until we were hoarse. "Come on, Charlie, let's you and I do the darned old dishes."

"We'll help too," our guests insisted. "We're old hands with a dish towel."

"You know, Frieda," Chick said, a little later, "it's hard to remember that you're a schoolteacher."

Setting down a plate, she eyed him severely. "That's enough from you, young man. Repeat this after me, if you please; stand straight and watch your diction:

> Then out spake brave Horatius,
> The Captain of the Gate . . ."

Chick joined her now, their voices blending together perfectly.

> " 'To every man upon this earth
> Death cometh soon or late. . . .' "

As they finished, he bowed from the waist. "Yes, ma'am. Go to thunder, ma'am."

"What are you two doing?" Jill asked. "Being silly or something?"

"Not now," Chick said. "Not any more."

CHAPTER 20

Chili Sauce, Esquire

UNTIL he was in third grade, Charlie had been our little boy. Now overnight in 1951, he outgrew all his clothes, slicked his hair impeccably, was at ease with girls and became an independent citizen. In addition, he led a pack of identical towheads who called him, "Hey you, Chili Sauce."

"He's coming along fine," Chick said, beaming at this transformation. "But I wish he'd put more meat on all that muscle."

"When he's on the jump every minute, how can he? Besides, look at us . . ."

"I know. I guess it's hopeless."

Thank goodness I've retired from retailing forever, I'd think as Chili Sauce and his buddies swarmed home from school, rifling our icebox and cupboards. Who'd want to miss these goings-on now? . . . What in thunder are those boys doing in the kitchen? Do I dare look?

Meantime Jill kept trying to build her brother's finesse. "Can't you walk without falling over things, Clumsy? Take those big snowshoe feet off the sofa. Are your hands and ears allergic to soap?"

"Mind your business, old flutterhead."

"But you're such a pig."

"You're not so wonderful, Jillie."

"Next to you I am, you crumb."

They love each other, I'd think, as this banter led to blows and howls. Jill used to lead Charles around by the nose, but she'd better not try it now.

"Why are you wearing lipstick and silk stockings?" he'd ask when they were on speaking terms again. "Because you're in seventh grade, must you be stupid?"

"Shush, you infant."

"It's silly. And it's a waste of money too. The girls in my class have more sense."

"Ho. If they speak to you, Ugly, they haven't. Anyhow, you're the one making a spectacle of himself around here lately. It's embarrassing. . . . Please, Mother, can't we stop that lemonade booth on the front lawn? He's begun to sell old toys and junk now . . . along with refreshments."

"I can't see why it should bother us really. You did the same thing, Jill, when you were seven. Don't you remember?"

"Well, I'm past that baby stuff now. And when boys come by . . ."

Bypassing his favorite subject for teasing, Charlie got down to business. "Say, speaking of junk, how about those puppets you don't use any more? Or some old books or jewelry? Can we have them for my store?"

"Well . . . if you help dry the dishes tonight . . ."

"Then it's a deal."

"You're really very generous, Jill," I said, "but aren't you stripping yourself to the bone?"

"Maybe. But this way my room stays cleaner. And if we encourage that boy, darn it, maybe he'll get fed-up sooner. What can we lose?"

Meantime Charlie's enthusiasm kept his trade expanding. Soon he had several of his pals as associates, some of them barking along the road, others selling, making change, keeping accounts and expediting deliveries. Stocks were plenteous and attractively displayed with price tickets. "Car was $2.00; now just 37 cents."

"A born executive," Chick said, "and a hustler too. At this rate, maybe he'll work his way through college . . . and I can retire."

Once cash came flowing into Charlie's fingers, it stuck there like cement. "We have to give some money to Red Cross at school," he'd say. "How about giving me some, Mom?"

When I suggested that he add a small personal donation to mine, he winced. "Touch the four dollars and seventy-seven cents I've saved? Heck no."

After further discussion didn't move him, I brought up another sore point. "Why do you carry every penny of your fortune to school every day? You could lose it. And aren't you being a show-off?"

"Listen, Mom. Kids today always bring all their money everywhere."

"Why?"

He took a long vehement breath. "Because this way . . . we feel *neat*."

"Neat?"

"Sure. Otherwise do you guess anyone would ever notice you?" Scattering a mountain of change from his purse, he began to count it lovingly. "Five cents . . . ten cents . . . twenty-five . . ."

"But Charlie, you know money isn't as wonderful as you like to believe it is."

"Who says it isn't?"

"Think of the things that you can't possibly buy at any price." When they had been enumerated, I asked for sheer pleasure, "Suppose I was old and hungry and shivering on a street corner. In a raggedy shawl too. And you came by with your millions. Would you buy me a cup of coffee?"

"No. I wouldn't."

"Are you serious?"

"Sure. Because anyhow, coffee isn't good for people."

Somehow we're failing with this child, I thought. Of

course he's at that miserly age. But what a sad specimen.

As his business prowess increased, Chili Sauce and his pals went downtown together increasingly in search of identical treasures: purses with special pockets, wallets and every type of bank from piggy style to cash register. When their funds were depleted by these whims, they went into new labors together: preparing gallons of lemonade, combing the neighborhood for handouts, raking leaves, digging crab grass, sweeping walks and cleaning cellars. "I was way down to three dollars and sixty-three cents," Charlie would confess, "but I'm working my way back to a five spot now."

Occasionally, when I needed to pay a tradesman, he was willing to loan from his hoard. "But give it back tomorrow, remember. Before supper."

"Suppose I forget?"

"Then I'll sue you."

"Murder," Jill said. "He's so tight he *creaks*."

Yet in February, Charlie was the only one of us who bought Winnie-the-Pooh a birthday gift. Producing a chocolate-scented toy and a new red collar, he drowned her with spoils. "Here you are, wuzza-wuzza. Stand up, pretty baby, and say thank you."

"Isn't that comic?" Jill whispered, tickled and yet torn by the paradox here. "He treats Winnie like a queen. But what did he give Daddy and me last time?

Calendars and penwipers as usual. In a couple of months, when your turn comes, Mother, I bet you'll get the same."

Charlie danced with anger. "You're just jealous, Slimey. Because Winnie loves me best."

"If she does, clean up after her next time."

"I will. She's my dog more than yours."

"Take her. Keep her and see if I care. Look how she wrecked my stockings, anyway, darn it."

While our son kept building his capital, Jill became increasingly poverty-stricken. "And isn't it hideous, Mother, when this is the very most important time of my life and I need *everything*? . . . I asked Charlie to please lend me seventy-five cents until next week; but he wouldn't."

"Times are hard all over, honey."

"They certainly are with us seventh-graders. I loan money to everyone always. And nobody ever pays me back."

"Why?"

"Partly because I forget to remind them. Then when I want to buy ice-cream sodas and lipsticks . . . it hurts."

"Well, if you'd like to earn some extra spending money, the garden needs weeding."

"Thanks. But I'm too busy."

"She'd better marry someone who can keep a roof over

her head," Chick would say, overhearing this conversation. "Otherwise she'll land in the poorhouse permanently."

"Oh Daddy, you know that won't happen."

"You keep on like this, young lady, and it will."

When Jill had gone off to her room, singing, he'd shake his head. "Who says raising kids is easy . . . especially when they go to such extremes?"

"Through Council meetings, we're doing our best. Aren't we, Chick?"

"I guess so. But lately it seems a little hopeless."

"Anyhow, they'll outgrow this."

"Ho. Who says so?"

During the week before my birthday, as always our home was buzzing with preparations. "Don't dare to go into my closet for anything," Chick warned. "There are some packages there which aren't to be touched."

"Stay out of my room on your life," Jill chorused. "If you need anything, be sure to ask me."

"That goes for me too . . . and you too," Charlie added. "Double."

Jill jerked to attention. "So what wonderful thing are you hiding there? . . . Another calendar?"

"You shut up," he said, turning crimson.

"This time can't you spend five cents of your savings?"

"Well . . . I'll have to see . . ."

As usual, during the next days, Charlie kept counting and recounting his money. But there seemed to be no joy in it; only pain. Why is he so depressed? I wondered. He's never been this way before.

Sometimes, looking up he'd ask me, "Isn't it the *thought* of a gift that matters?"

"Of course."

"Did you like what I made last year?"

"It's beautiful. I use it every day."

"Do you want anything *else* very much, Mom?"

"I don't think so. Let's see. Daddy's going to give me a bed jacket, I hope. And a box of candy. . . . But . . . let's see. I certainly could use a new penwiper and some handmade place cards . . ."

Finally, when we had been through this quizzing game a dozen times he asked, "What would you like very best in the world?"

"Something you've taken trouble to make yourself, Charlie."

His face fell. "How about perfume? You said once . . ."

"Perfume? You know I could almost eat it."

"That's what I thought. Isn't what comes in the biggest bottle the nicest?"

"That depends . . ." Let's get off this subject fast, I

thought. The sooner the better. . . . "Say, son, what kind of a cake should I make this time?"

"Well" — his face brightened again — "well, you know Jill won't eat chocolate lately; she says her face gets too bumpy . . ."

"How about your favorite, sponge layers with caramel frosting?"

"Perfect . . . with butter-pecan ice cream. And we'll open the presents after dessert."

The afternoon of the big day, Charlie and his partners closed shop early and went downtown together. Eventually they came streaming back into the kitchen, laden with packages. "Gee, can we lick up that bowl, Mrs. Carey? Say, that cake smells good."

"Keep those fingers away, please."

"Can't we have just a nibble?"

"No sir. Not till tomorrow."

Until I finished spreading the frosting, they lay sprawled on the dining-room carpet, each boy counting his money. "Gee, I spent more than I meant to. Crumb, I've got to sweat some more now."

"What did you invest in today . . . more strong lockers?" I hollered.

"Come on. Stop ribbing us."

"How's business lately?"

"Super. Say, can we get at that bowl now?"

"Yes. Come help yourselves."

"I got to do a special job now," Charlie said briskly, excusing himself. "You know why, guys. I'll see you subsequently."

"O.K., Chili Sauce. You'd better pack it in plenty of paper."

"Is he sick or something?" I asked. "He's never done this before."

"No. But he's busy. This is your birthday, isn't it?"

"Very much so. I can't wait."

"Think you'll get anything good tonight?"

"I certainly hope so."

"Ho. Ho. This year, for a change, everybody might forget you. Old Chili Sauce especially."

"Don't be so cruel."

"Ho. Ho. Ho."

Dinner that night was a very special occasion, with our fanciest tablecloth, china and silver. After the inevitable comments about extra dishes to wash, we got into the festive spirit. "This roast is cooked to perfection," Chick said, slicing it approvingly. "Thank goodness we're back to normal with no outside help underfoot. This is the way it *should* be."

Eventually, after we had dished out the ice cream, the children darkened the lights and brought in the cake. "Happy Birthday, dear Mother . . ." "Make a wish before you blow out the candles," Jill commanded, "and notice there are only *eight* this year. For laughs."

A *wish*, I thought. Can't I think of something I *want?*

"Come on, Mom," Charlie shouted. "Stop holding up the parade, will you?"

Looking at him intently, I found and made my wish.

"Bull's-eye," he cried as in one breath the candles flickered out. "Did you ask for something good?"

"Yes, son. I think I did."

Now came gift-opening time, with the children's presents last at their insistence. Together we exclaimed over a large box of mixed chocolates and the usual joke-surprises: dining-room candles, ink, a kitchen spatula and some dog biscuits for Winnie. Next there were endless books, a fountain pen and a quilted bed jacket from Chick. "I hope it's what you want and frothy enough. Otherwise, Ernie . . ."

"It's beautiful. Exquisite. I intend to live in it."

As I reached for Jill's package, she gasped with anticipation. Removing the card from its envelope, I struggled with her most stylish handwriting. "This is a long poem, everybody. So let's listen carefully. . . ."

After we had oohed and aahed over her talent together, I opened one box, then smaller and smaller ones in sequence. "You must have spent hours on this, you jokester. Am I going to finish with a goose egg?"

"Keep going, Mother," she chortled. "You'll find out."

Eventually I came to a pin and matching earrings, each boasting large, pink, embalmed roses. "It's what I wanted badly, myself, Mom," Jill whispered. "Aren't they lovely?"

We kissed each other, almost in tears, while Chick murmured something about sentimental women and renditions of "Hearts and Flowers."

Meantime Charlie seemed to be suffocating as his gifts lay waiting. Observing his pain, Jill nudged me.

"What can this be?" I asked, opening a large grimy envelope first. "Not a penwiper and some lovely place cards? Oh thank you. Thank you."

"Hurry, Mom, get the next one now. Quick."

Again the wrapping job showed every sign of loving seven-year-old fingers. "What — something else here too?" I was busily tearing away paper now. "It looks too big for a calendar. Unless that box-within-a-box routine is coming again."

"Take it easy. This might break," he roared as I began to paw through a tangle of tissue paper. "Watch it, will you?"

At last I lifted out a sort of beribboned urn filled with emerald liquid. "What? Lily of the Valley perfume? Oh. Oh. Oh."

"You see, it smelled the strongest, Mom, so . . ."

Opening it professionally, I dabbed some of the liquid over my neck and wrists. "Mmmmmmm. Delicious."

"I'll say it's strong," Chick said from his end of the table. "Whew."

Jill had begun to cough. "What is that smell again, Charlie? *Lilies?*"

After scrutinizing us one by one, Charlie asked, "What's the matter? It's O.K., isn't it?"

"Of course. Perfect. The answer to my birthday wish."

CHAPTER 21

To Do a Thing Together

DURING the next two years the children's activities increased until we were dizzy. "Scouts, dancing, choir, dramatics, sports, Sunday School, piano lessons, tooth-straightening," Chick groaned, tabulating them on his fingers. "What's responsible for this razzle-dazzle, Ernie? Can't we put a stop to it somehow?"

"Would you want Jill and Charlie sitting home in their rooms all day?"

"Of course not. But at this rate they're covering more mileage than Burton Holmes."

Fortunately by now I had gathered the stamina to take my turn at taxiing. But increasingly before we finished with one of Jill's pursuits, we were starting fresh with Charlie. "The Girl Scouts are meeting the same night as the Cubs?" Chick would ask. "How can we be both places at once? Hell and Maria."

Still, in spite of our faster tempo and ever-widening interests, we continued to enjoy family times together. Since the living room seemed especially "cozy and comfyish," we gathered there Saturdays and Sundays, each immersed in separate interests. Usually Jill would be prone on the floor, cutting out a new skirt or dress. Close by, Charlie would be pasting his baseball-hero scrapbook. While Chick thumbed through a garden catalogue, I'd swish through newspapers, tossing them over my shoulder page by page.

"Mercy, Mrs. Carey," Jill would tease, imitating the dressing-down delivered years before, "are you responsible for this mess? For shame."

I'd review the carnage of cloth snippings, patterns and pins. "Speaking of cyclones, how are *you?*"

"Marigolds," Chick would intone, ignoring this nonsense. "Odorless ones, Ernie. Let's try them this year."

"Yes, let's. Around that compost pile particularly. . . . And do you know that every neighbor on the block is dumping his grass clippings here?"

"Why not? I asked them to do it as a special favor."

Oh dear, I'd think. On subjects like this, we never get anywhere.

"Hey, Mom," Charlie would sing out, "can I have today's *Times* now? There's the neatest picture of Campanella. Don't throw it away."

"There's a new hairdo there too, Mom," Jill would chant. "Don't throw that away either."

"All right. All right." . . . Then a minute later, I'd quote a gossip-column * treasure. "Listen to this: 'Daddy

* Sylvester; *Daily News*

Grace, the midwest prophet, believes in the old *Cheaper by the Dozen* adage. He just got delivery on his twelfth Cadillac. . . .' That's something, isn't it? And we're still driving that old red convertible."

Any reference to a car always wrenched us from our individual delights like a bombshell. "How about it, Dad? Can we get a Cadillac? Betty's family has a beautiful new blue one. . . . Come on, Mom. Can't we get a natsy new superflow? They hit ninety miles an hour."

"Let's save this for our next Council meeting."

"Can't we decide it now?"

"Must we?"

"Well, tomorrow then. After dinner. O.K.?"

"O.K."

Observing the children, it was hard to realize that they had grown so much. Jill, a freshman in high school by 1953, was tall as I, and "the spit and image." Charlie, a fifth-grader, was indeed his father's Junior, unconsciously duplicating his stride, his laugh and prowess in athletics. "C'mon, Dad. . . . How about it, Dad? . . . Hey, Maestro, our Red Sox really wilted them, didn't they? What a massacre."

The mementos of their efforts to date were evident on our tables, mantelpiece and walls: calendars, pottery ash trays, a clay imprint of Charlie's blunt little hand, a silhouette of Jill by Jill, 1949, a cross-stitched bit of embroidery with its red-and-white-and-blue message: "I will dwell in the house of the Lord . . . C.E.C. Jr. . . . 1953". . . and a framed poem that Jill had composed for Chick's last birthday:

> A smile is always on your face
> And though your jokes may be corn
> To be with you for a little while
> Makes me glad that I was born . . .

"They're irreplaceable of course," Chick said, as one treasure was added to the next, "but if you contribute an umbrella stand to this clutter, Ern, it will be the last straw."

Since Chick's precious old baseball photograph had long since crumbled to dust, it no longer bisected our mirror. But my seventeenth-century little man continued to hang in a prominent spot among the etchings, water colors and pictures we had added.

Other mementos from Chick's and my business friends were here too . . . some of them, like the children's engraved silver, serving as candy dishes and cigarette containers. ("Let's use them," they had insisted. "This way, they'll be shined up and pretty.")

Almost as important to me were the gifts received on my two retirements from retailing. Especially the copy of a book carrying a message and the sixteen signatures of fellow metropolitan-area buyers when I left their fraternity forever:

From our fold you are going
To the world you are showing
The talent that put you on top.
The Best Seller List was the guide for our shopping
So we picked the cream of the crop.

"Gee, it's hard to remember you were in business, Mom," Jill said, repeating this message frowningly. "Won't you tell me about it some day? Was it easy and lots of fun?"

"Another knickknack, Ernie," Chick moaned as I added this keepsake to the rest. "Do you want excursion buses stopping here eventually? . . . 'P.S. The place is charming.' "

"Mercy, no. But the attic won't hold another thing. Besides, familiar odds and ends seem so good."

"But enough is enough."

Though my attic-hoarding habits had been a bone of contention for years, eventually it became an issue. And all because young Charlie, in earning a Cub Scout silver arrow, had to eliminate all home fire hazards. "Must we?" I wailed, knowing that we must cooperate regardless. "All right. But tread gently. Rather than destroy one irreplaceable piece of paper, I'll rip out my heart and eat it."

"If you want sympathy, Ern," Chick said, starting up the stairs with a load of wastebaskets, "look in the dictionary."

Woe. A thousand times woe.

Since the children seemed to consider Operation Attic a special lark, they clambered after us merrily. "Gee, Mom. Look at this squirrel nest here. Boy oh boy."

Smoothing one of the cartons, I bowed my head. " 'Is it nothing to you, all ye that pass by? behold, and see if there be any sorrow like unto my sorrow.' "

Disregarding the boxes of old manuscripts, scrapbooks, letters and diaries, the children dived into those holding more golden rewards. Discovering old diplomas, napkin rings, wedding souvenirs, the curtains used in Linville, a maid's uniform from East Ninetieth Street days, family photographs and a baby potty, they went crazy.

"Look, everybody," Charlie cried, seizing a snapshot of himself in christening clothes, "isn't this *good?* I'm going to keep it in my room."

Jill had been handling the potty reverently. "This was mine once *really?* I must have been pint-sized."

Soon she had segregated all the items connected with her birth: letters, a dried corsage, miniature yellow mittens and bootees. "What does this telegram mean?" She held up a sheath of them. " 'Dear Ern. Congratulations. Please tell her early in life that the cash discount is two per cent not five . . .' Is it a joke or something?"

"Your mother should have been a junk dealer," Chick said, struggling with a trunk.

At last I came upon a dress, red, scanty and sporting a

Paris label. Holding it against my shoulders, I wondered if I could get into it still. Maybe so.

"Wow," Jill said, falling over the baby potty in her excitement. "Who ever wore that hot potato? Where's the rest of it?"

"What do you mean? It's all here."

"Really? . . . If I should need to wear a comic costume sometime, can I borrow this, Mom?"

"Of course. Things should always be used."

"O.K. We're talking about having a variety show at school. I might be dancing in a chorus or something."

"If it comes off, give me plenty of warning, will you? Or you may wind up as Miss Washday again."

"Yikes. Once was enough."

"It happens that I'm very fond of this dress," I said, folding it away carefully. "Thank goodness our boys didn't see it and salvage it. Eh?"

"Well, Ern," Chick said later, as we examined our handiwork, "this place is clean as a whistle . . . but our trash cans are almost empty. What the hell happened?"

". . . Jill found some things she could use. . . . Charlie found others . . . and . . ."

Our son came up the ladder, Cub book in hand. "Hey, Dad, will you give me a check mark for this job? It's all I need for that arrow."

Chick bent and signed his name with a flourish.

"While you're here, Charlie," I said, "suppose you start hauling back some of those cartons. Who wants them piled downstairs underfoot?"

"Thank goodness you saved that batch of old letters," Chick grunted as Charlie placed them in his arms. "Some of these stamps may be valuable some day."

I stopped humming long enough to nod my head.

Since a year of Girl Scouting hadn't been easy for me, I was happy that Chick carried the major responsibility of Charlie's pack. Once a month, when we gathered for meetings, he presided while I relaxed. But before these get-togethers, we always went through a horrible time getting our son into uniform.

At the last moment, Jill would be on the phone borrowing a cap from a neighbor, while Chick shined shoes, I removed a trouser spot and Charlie looked frantically for his corded kerchief-loop. "Jeepers. If I don't find it, the entire den will be in the soup."

We'd charge into the school, red-faced and winded. Later, while Chick made announcements and surveyed his ninety-odd lads benignly, I'd chat with the other mothers. "The routine's strict. But don't the boys respond beautifully? . . . Did you have the crisis we did tonight, Ern? Jimmy's here in argyle socks and sneakers; I could die."

Soon after one of the Cub evenings, Jill announced that she would need that red dress next Friday. "The show's been cooking for several weeks. And four of us will do the Charleston."

During the next few days she kept practicing steps and fussing with alterations on my treasure. "Shouldn't the skirt be even tighter, Mother? How did you wear your hair, slinky or glamour-puss? How about stockings and shoes?"

"Must you duplicate me exactly, dear?"

"Why not? It will be hilarious. Now tell me about jewelry."

"You'll need dangling earrings, dozens of bracelets and long ropes of pearls. I had some, but we got rid of them, darn it."

"Mother, you didn't. You mean you kept all those old papers and tossed out jewelry? How awful."

"I know. It was stupid."

"Can't that child talk about anything but this show?" Chick asked as we girls conferred endlessly. "Don't they assign any work at school ever?"

But like the rest of us, he was enjoying the excitement. Whistling "Charleston" over and over, he kept chiding himself, "Drat that tune. Must it haunt me forever?"

The big night, double-circled on our family calendar, came at last. Since Jill was dining and dressing at a friend's home, the other three of us were able to be fairly calm. But time dragged until we rushed off and took our seats in the auditorium. "I hope she doesn't forget her part," Charlie said, remembering an experience he had had recently. "If she does, I'll dive down on the floor."

"Last time we practiced, she was perfect," Chick said reassuringly. "She's the best little dancer I know anywhere."

Meantime as always I had been chatting with neighbors. After a false alarm or two, the lights dimmed, the curtains opened and we lost ourselves in a minstrel show. "Mistaaah Jasper . . . will you be so kind as to fetch that pail of water, Mistaaah Jasper."

"Hell and Maria," Chick murmured. "They haven't changed a line from the time I was fetching that water myself."

Jill's act came at the very end of the show. As the piano struck the opening chords, she led a chorus of young ladies across the stage.

Charleston, Charleston . . .

As time veered back overwhelmingly, my head throbbed. Step — kick. Step — kick. Ah, how debonnaire Chick had looked that night. "Your name is Ernestine? Any relation to the singer?"

"Afraid not. My mother's an industrial engineer."

"Did she ever tell you that good men are scarce?"

Behind us, a long, hungry whistle jerked me back to

reality. "Hey, Bud, pipe the job in red. Who is she? What a gas-pump figure."

"Ssssh," the answer came cracking up into a soprano, "that's Jill, you jerk. Her folks can hear you."

How graceful and grown-up our little girl seemed tonight. How vivacious. Clearly the problems of adolescence would be more complicated soon. But I would be home, fortunately . . . and able to share them for better or worse.

Beside me, Chick had been sitting transfixed. "Good Lord," he sighed. "That child is you a while back, honey. Where did she dig up that dress? Yowee."

But during the encore, he returned to his role as father. "Isn't Jill's getup too brief? It fits like a banana skin."

"Grandpa, how you've changed. Once upon a time you enjoyed a little cheesecake."

"I do still. But not on my daughter."

After returning home, we gathered in the kitchen, as usual, for ice cream and Cokes. "Let's put on a family show, Daddy," Jill said, taking his arm. "Our first act, folks, will be Mr. Charles and Miss Jill Carey, famous dance team. Everybody sing now . . ."

"Come on," Charlie said. "If they can swing it, we can too." We galloped off together, disregarding Winnie, who was yipping at our heels.

"Don't give up, you pantywaists," Chick said as one

by one we sat down exhausted. "Don't show the white feather." Then after fetching a pail from under the sink, "Maybe you'd like Mistaaah Jasper to . . ."

"Daddy, you're nice," Jill said. "Some day my husband will be exactly like you."

He doffed an imaginary hat.

"And you're O.K. too, Mom. Really."

Chick put his arms around us both. "My two best girls," he said, squeezing hard.

Charlie came clattering into the huddle. "But boys are *much* better. Aren't they, Dad?"

Today, the little verse which Mother wrote for our very first kitchen hangs, as always, near the stove. "What's this? Why is it here?" friends ask, examining it. Then they read aloud:

To do a thing together
Gives it an added zest
This is our place for teamwork
To plan, perform and rest.